CONTINENTAL DRIFT

THE ROYAL SOCIETY OF CANADA

Special Publications

CONTINENTAL

DRIFT

THE ROYAL SOCIETY OF CANADA
SPECIAL PUBLICATIONS, NO. 9

Edited by G. D. Garland, F.R.S.C.

PUBLISHED BY THE UNIVERSITY OF TORONTO PRESS
IN CO-OPERATION WITH
THE ROYAL SOCIETY OF CANADA
1966

PREFACE

THE POSSIBILITY that the continents of the earth have undergone major changes in position during the earth's history has fascinated scholars for at least three hundred years. Recently, evidence from several scientific disciplines has shown that the possibility must be very seriously considered in any study of the surface features of the earth.

The first part of the present volume consists of papers given at a symposium on continental drift, held at the annual meeting of the Royal Society of Canada in Charlottetown in June 1964. They present the views of three geophysicists, a botanist, and an astronomer. In these papers, the present evidence for or against continental drift is reviewed and the authors in most cases draw their own conclusions. The reader will find that there is not unanimous agreement in favour of drift.

Nearly all discussions of continental drift stress the possible separation of the Americas from Europe and Africa. Considerable work has been done on the tracing of structures, on each side of the Atlantic Ocean, which might once have been connected. Geologists and geophysicists working in the Arctic or on the eastern seaboard of Canada have an important contribution to make to this subject. The second part of this volume, therefore, consists of a group of papers, also presented at the Charlottetown meeting, which throw light on the complicated crustal structure of these regions. In any attempt to reconstruct North America as part of Europe the features described in these papers will have to be taken into account. Once again, the reader will find differences of opinion on the question of whether the evidence favours a separation of our continent from Europe. Indeed, it is because the theory of continental drift is so difficult to confirm without ambiguity by direct observation that it remains controversial but exciting.

G. D. G.

CONTENTS

CONTRIBUTORS

JON BERGER, *Institute of Oceanography, Dalhousie University, Halifax, Nova Scotia*

J. E. BLANCHARD, *Institute of Oceanography, Dalhousie University, Halifax, Nova Scotia*

H. L. CAMERON,* *Nova Scotia Research Foundation, Halifax, Nova Scotia*

A. E. COK, *Institute of Oceanography, Dalhousie University, Halifax, Nova Scotia*

ERNST R. DEUTSCH, *Physics Department, Memorial University of Newfoundland, St. John's, Newfoundland*

A. K. GOODACRE, *Dominion Observatory, Ottawa, Ontario*

M. J. KEEN, *Institute of Oceanography, Dalhousie University, Halifax, Nova Scotia*

GORDON J. F. MACDONALD, *Institute of Geophysics and Planetary Physics, University of California, Los Angeles, California*

E. NYLAND, *Institute of Oceanography, Dalhousie University, Halifax, Nova Scotia*

B. R. PELLETIER, *Bedford Institute of Oceanography, Dartmouth, Nova Scotia*

N. W. RADFORTH, *Department of Biology, Hamilton College, McMaster University, Hamilton, Ontario*

R. W. TANNER, *Dominion Observatory, Ottawa, Ontario*

J. T. WILSON, *Department of Physics, University of Toronto, Toronto, Ontario*

*Deceased, October 1965.

PART I

Current Ideas on Continental Drift

SOME RULES FOR CONTINENTAL DRIFT

J. T. Wilson, F.R.S.C.

NO IDEA that has been discussed for three hundred years, has been debated vigorously for fifty, and is today a centre of controversy can properly be ignored. So it is with the observation that the shores on the two sides of the Atlantic Ocean are similar in shape and nearly parallel and the theory that this may have been caused by the drift of continents.

In several recent books and symposia, the hypothesis of continental drift has been strongly supported. However, its validity is denied or regarded with scepticism by many scholars. I shall not attempt to resolve the conflict. Indeed I am not sure what would be accepted as final proof that drift had occurred, but I consider that the arguments in favour of it are sufficiently important to justify making the assumption that it has occurred in order to discuss what its precise nature could have been.

My first objective is to ascertain exactly what is under discussion, for one difficulty about the hypothesis of drift has been that it comprises not one but an infinity of possible theories, all but one of which must be wrong. Any careful examination of the literature will show that no two authors have agreed upon the same pattern of drift. Some of the most ardent advocates have done the theory great disservice by supporting versions that other specialists could see at once were outrageous.

In order to understand discussions about drift it is fundamental to realize that the arguments about it resolve themselves into three parts. The first question is whether drift has occurred. Once the occurrence of drift is admitted or assumed, the next question concerns the choice of a particular pattern and history of drift to fit observations. The third question to be answered is that of the nature of the mechanism that has caused drift.

The first problem requires the adjustment of one's view to enable one to consider objectively whether the evidence suggests that drift has actually occurred. Alfred Wegener did this and produced several arguments in proof of drift, which have been widely ignored but never satisfactorily answered by other solutions. Nevertheless, it is generally hard to achieve such objectivity.

For many years my own opposition to the idea of drift was based upon my field-work in the Canadian Shield. I could see that in Precambrian time, the metamorphic rocks had been mountain-built and greatly distorted, but since that time the Shield seemed to have been deformed hardly at all. Around most of the perimeter, Lower Palaeozoic strata lap undisturbed

3

upon the older rocks with little trace of mobility or distortion. Nothing could appear more rigid or unchanging. In those places where the margin is faulted, as in the Ottawa valley, the disturbances are minor and local. For a long time I could not equate this evidence of immobility with drifting, during the Mesozoic and Cenozoic eras, but now I believe that drift could have occurred, the disturbances accompanying it being concentrated at any particular time in narrow zones with other large regions seeming to move without noticeable deformation.

The second problem is to decide from the infinite choice of possible paths which one has been the correct pattern of movement of the continents.

We are so used to thinking about a fixed geography essentially invariable throughout time, with permanent ocean basins and continents, that most advocates of the drift theory have failed to realize that once the idea of drift is considered, an infinity of palaeogeographies become possible, and the task is to choose the single correct evolutionary pattern from them. While maintaining a belief in the occurrence of drift, it is possible to change one's ideas about the patterns by which it occurred.

The acceptance of the notion of drift upsets many preconceived ideas. The problem is to determine which concepts still remain valid and which can be disturbed.

This paper is concerned chiefly with a search for the rules that have governed drift if it has occurred.

S. W. Carey's great contributions to structural geology (1958) are to my mind obscured and his arguments weakened when he suggests straightening out the bend in the Alaskan cordillera or opening a vast space between the Brazilian and Guayana shields. These regions are relatively well known and as far as I know, most Alaskan and South American geologists produce strong arguments for disagreeing with Carey. Had he suggested bending part of the East Pacific Rise or opening a basin beside it, no one might have known enough to object strongly. Had he even confined distortion within the limits of the Andes and the Alaska orogenies, one might find it hard to disagree, but proposals involving gross distortion of stable shields or other inactive regions appear unjustified. I believe it should be possible to define rules of what did happen and what did not happen during periods of drifting.

The object of this paper is thus a limited one. It will assume that drift has occurred and has followed certain definite rules. It will search for those rules using a few specific regions as a guide, for it would be foolish to try to rewrite all geology in a short paper. Should these rules prove generally acceptable, the formidable task of applying them to the development of the history of all the earth will remain.

It is not necessary to know the mechanism in order to believe that some process has occurred. Man knew of the existence of thunderstorms and of the earth's magnetic field long before he could account for them. A discussion of the possible mechanism is therefore not necessary and will not be attempted here; but it is considered that the discussion of rules will be clearer if it is pointed out that a particular mechanism has been proposed which appears capable of causing drift, and if it is further assumed that this mechanism has been operating.

This mechanism was first put forward by Holmes (1931), who suggested that convection currents rise under mid-ocean ridges and sink under island arcs and continental mountains. Inasmuch as there is only one system of ridges and one system of mountains on the earth, it has already been pointed out that there may be only one convection cell operating at present and that this is a very long and tortuous one (Wilson 1963). Its surface pattern is illustrated in Figure 1. This diagram is based upon surface topography and geology with some guidance from the location of earthquakes. However, lacking direct evidence, one cannot be sure whether convection currents exist or not and, if they do, whether or not they follow closely the pattern of ridges and mountains.

We shall assume further following Hess (1962) and Dietz (1962), that the continents are rafts of siliceous material that cannot be carried down by current, and that the ocean floors are merely the altered top of the mantle, coming up along mid-ocean ridges and sinking again in ocean trenches.

The surface rocks are rigid and brittle, so that if flow is to occur it must be at a depth where the rocks are hot. Seismologists have identified a layer at a depth of from 50 to 400 kilometres which has low seismic velocities and which may be near the melting point. We shall assume that convection occurs up to the top of this layer and that the crust and top of the mantle above it are carried about like brittle plates of ice on a stream. According to this view distortion is concentrated in narrow belts between plates.

The earth's surface may be distorted in several ways, with each of which we associate specific geological phenomena: by dilatation with grabens and rifts, by shearing with large transcurrent faults, by compression with mountain-building, and by flow with metamorphic terrains. These will now be considered.

CLASSIFICATION OF GRABENS

First we shall consider tension, which is generally thought to find expression in grabens and rifts. We shall start by attempting to classify the first of these.

All books on structural geology define grabens as structurally depressed blocks, with more or less parallel sides, bounded by normal faults and having a length considerably greater than their breadth. Although these have been shown normally to have faults on both sides, more recent work shows that some grabens have faults only on one side and that the other side is merely bent down. Certain of the rift grabens in Kenya are of this type. Some geologists place no limitation on their size, but following Hills (1963), we shall exclude here all minor features less than 10 miles long that might be fortuitous aspects of a faulted terrain rather than significant indicators of

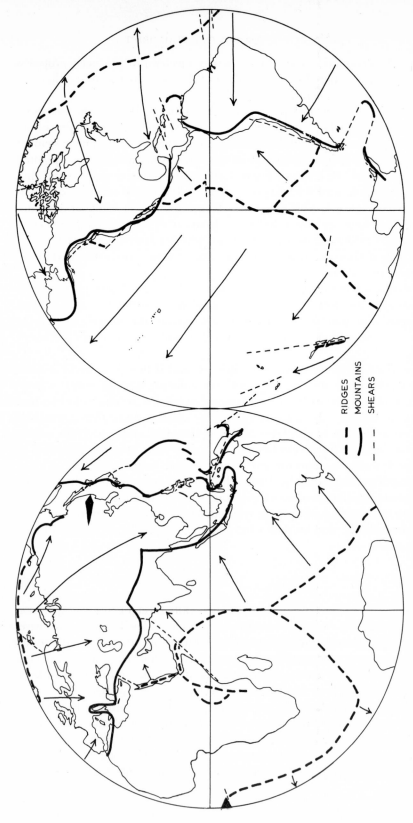

FIGURE 1. Sketch map showing compressional mountains, mid-ocean rifts, and approximate directions of the sub-surface currents assumed to flow from one to the other.

downward or tensional movement. Table I presents an outline classification of grabens with type examples.

TABLE I

TYPES OF GRABENS AND FAULTED TRENCHES

Class	Type of example	Length	Regional association
1. Great rifts	East African rift valleys	Thousands of miles	Tension— formation of ocean basins
2. Coastal grabens	Bahia graben, Brazil	Hundreds of miles	Tension— formation of ocean basins
3. Longitudinal grabens in primary mountains	Vale of Chile	Hundreds of miles	Compression— mountain-building
4. Continental grabens springing from secondary mountains	Rhine graben	Hundreds of miles	Compression— mountain-building
5. Submarine trenches with island arcs and primary mountains	Aleutian trench	Hundreds of miles	Compression— mountain-building
6. Ocean deeps along fracture zones	Romanche deep, Atlantic Ocean	Hundreds of miles	Shearing

GREAT RIFTS

Great length, extensive volcanism, strong seismicity, and in many places, high marginal uplift distinguish the class of great rifts from all other grabens. The classic example is the system of East African rift valleys.

Concerning their main features, there is no doubt. A connected system of grabens or fault troughs, each commonly 20 to 40 miles wide, a few hundred miles long, and thousands of feet deep, extends from the Red Sea to the Zambesi River opposite Madagascar.

The whole rift lies along the crest of high ground, of which the well-marked upland surfaces have been shown to have been uplifted in Mesozoic and Tertiary times. Associated with the great rift are most of the active volcanoes of Africa, widespread Tertiary lavas, and numerous earthquakes.

This system has been described well by Dixey (1956), but much work has been done since then. The nature of the rifts is still a subject of controversy. Although an origin due to compression was at one time strongly advocated, nearly everyone now agrees that the rifts were formed by tension or at least relief of pressure. Their origin is generally held to be associated with that of the adjacent uplands.

In east and central Africa, all the lavas and movements are agreed to be of Upper Miocene age or younger. W. Pulfrey (see Dixey 1956) found no earlier structures there, and B. H. Baker (personal communication) considers that this was at least the dominant age of formation of the whole system. On the other hand, Dixey (1956, p. 38) holds that "the rifts do

seem to have arisen from some ancient deep-seated or fundamental weakness of the crust, which in Precambrian times expressed itself at great
depth in immense thrusts and shear zones, and in the Jurassic, the Tertiary,
and post-Tertiary, gave rise in the upper levels to an intermittent arching
of the crust associated with more or less contemporaneous rifting along
parallel normal faults." From this description, it seems clear that although
the rifts may in places have followed Precambrian structures, those structures were not themselves rifts. The evidence, he adds, also suggests that
the ends of the rift system may be Jurassic in age and hence older than the
centre. If so, this may be because these parts were affected by the opening
of the Red Sea to the north and the sinking or separation of the Mozam-
bique Geosyncline and Channel in the south.

The rift valleys of Africa proper lead directly into the Red Sea. The
seismicity, volcanism, and structural pattern suggest that they are parts
of the same system, but the Red Sea is older than the rifts in east Africa,
the Somaliland coast having been uplifted between Middle Eocene and
Lower Miocene times (Dixey 1956, p. 32).

Girdler (1963) and Drake and Girdler (1964) have recently given
a full geophysical study of the Red Sea and compared it with other rifts.
They conclude that the Red Sea and Arabian Gulf are directly connected
with, and structurally similar to, the African rifts, but that the continental
crust has been separated by rotation of part of it through 6° to 9° about
a fulcrum north of the Gulf of Aqaba, forming a deep axial trough up to
70 km wide bounded by shallower terraces. I suggest that part of the
opening of the Red Sea could have been taken up by shearing, which has
been mapped along the Jordan Valley. Rock samples and gravity and
magnetic anomalies over the deep suggest that the continental crust is there
replaced by dense, basic intrusive dykes. Girdler quotes an age of early
Miocene (25,000,000 years) for the origin of these rifts. It is now generally
believed that the rift proper is only as wide as the central deep and not
as wide as the Red Sea.

Girdler follows the view of Heezen and Ewing (1960) that the Red Sea
and Arabian Gulf rifts are continuous with and part of the world system
of mid-ocean ridges. Similarities in volcanism, seismicity, gravity and magnetic anomalies, and the topography of the rift itself support this view. The
mid-ocean ridge system is supposed to include the line of separation of
the entire Indian and Atlantic oceans and to cross the southeastern part
of the Pacific Ocean. With the evidence that the rifting of the Atlantic
Ocean began about Jurassic time (Wilson, 1965), we are led to the conclusion that the three rifts may represent an evolutionary sequence as shown
in Table II.

Several geologists have suggested that some of the great ridges of the
western Pacific, although aseismic and without active volcanoes, form
part of the world-wide rift system. If so, they perhaps represent a fourth
inactive and older stage in the evolutionary cycle. On the other hand the

TABLE II

STAGES IN THE EVOLUTION OF GREAT RIFTS

| Type | Age of origin | Characteristic width of rift (km) | |
		Central deep	Total
1. East African	Upper Miocene (12,000,000 yr)	0	50
2. Red Sea	Lower Miocene (25,000,000 yr)	<70	500
3. Atlantic Ocean	Upper Jurassic (150,000,000 yr)	500	5000

graben across Iceland, which has been reinterpreted by Walker (1960), presents the best view of oceanic rifting.

COASTAL GRABENS

Opening off the margin of several continents is a series of small down-faulted basins or grabens. Several are of Cretaceous or Tertiary age, but another group, which may be of the same origin, is Palaeozoic.

The Bahia graben is located approximately 500 miles south of the eastern-most point of Brazil. It extends for 300 miles northward from the coast, and has an average width of 50 miles. Because it contains the only pro-ducing oilfields in Brazil, it has been well mapped and drilled. The southern part, known as the Reconcavo, contains up to 7500 feet of Cretaceous strata resting upon a Precambrian basement. Across a buried ridge, the northern part also contains Cretaceous and probably down-faulted Silurian rocks. The whole structure has been considered to have been initiated and gradu-ally deepened during Cretaceous time, as a consequence of the rifting of the Gondwanaland continent (Taylor 1952; Mesner and Woolridge 1964).

The Marajo graben lies hidden under alluvium at the mouth of the Amazon River, but has been outlined by seismic surveys and drilled to a depth of 13,000 feet without reaching basement. It is about 10,000 square miles in area. The marine clastic sediments, chiefly sandstones, that fill the basin show that it also was formed during Cretaceous and Lower Tertiary time (Oliveira 1951).

The Norwegian channel is a sickle-shaped depression 500 miles long and 40 to 50 miles wide which follows closely the south coast of Norway from the Scandic Sea up the Skagerrak to the east coast of Sweden. It has been considered to be down-faulted, perhaps in post-Cretaceous time, and hence is not connected with the older Oslo graben. In Denmark, beds of volcanic ash of Eocene age may have been derived from volcanoes in the channel. It is still marked by occasional earthquakes (Holtedahl 1950).

In the Canadian Arctic Archipelago, Fortier and Morley (1956) have drawn attention to evidence of widespread Tertiary faulting and uplift. They divide Baffin Island into four blocks, each of which has been uplifted on the northeast side and tilted down to the southwest. Valleys extending northwestwards through Cumberland Sound, Frobisher Bay, and from the south coast separate these blocks. They also state that "a sharp discontinuity at the south coast of Devon Island along an aeromagnetic profile that crosses Lancaster Sound is substantial ground for believing that a major dislocation in basement rocks has occurred at that point on the coast. Normal faulting has been recognized in many areas of that region and topographic depressions are known to be bounded by steep fault scarps" (p. 10).

Aktapok Island in Ungava Bay, which opens off Hudson Strait, is formed of Ordovician strata, generally believed to be down-faulted. It is thus probable that Lancaster Sound, Hudson Strait, and probably other channels in the Archipelago are grabens of late Cretaceous or Tertiary age.

The Indian Ocean coast of Somaliland and Kenya has been considered to be a fault. In Tanganyika at the southern end, owing to a bend in the coast, this fault extends inland to form part of a graben again containing a thick section of Cretaceous and Tertiary rocks.

Another structure that should perhaps be mentioned here is the Cameroun graben or rift described by Geze (1953). Although often included with the great rifts, it is isolated from that system.

There are therefore several grabens around the coasts of the Atlantic and Indian oceans which are of similar age and dimensions and all of which open to the ocean at one end. It seems probable that if drift occurred, they were formed as a consequence of the opening of the oceans. Except for the Cameroun rift and perhaps the Norwegian Channel, they were not the sites of volcanic activity. Those that have been investigated contain down-faulted basement rocks indicating that dilatation has not gone far enough to open rifts.

One is justified in regarding these grabens as a separate class. A search would probably reveal other possible examples. Among older grabens requiring classification are those at Oslo, Adelaide, and in Tasmania. Possibly these should be included here.

Longitudinal Grabens in Primary Mountains

At intervals down the whole length of the Cordillera and Andean systems of the Americas are long valleys lying between coastal mountains of contorted sedimentary rocks of the graywacke facies and inner arcs of volcanic and igneous mountains. These valleys include Cook Inlet, some of the islets of the Alaska Panhandle, the Hecate and Georgia straits in British Columbia, Puget Sound, the Great Valley of California, valleys in the Andes of Columbia and Ecuador, and the Vale of Chile.

Many authors refer to these valleys as grabens, and no doubt they are in places bounded by and depressed along faults. On the other hand, if one follows the view of Umbgrove (1947) as developed by Jacobs, Russell, and Wilson (1959), it would seem that the faulting was incidental and that the valleys have developed as geosynclines throughout their history. They may be distinguished readily from the two previous classes of grabens because they lie longitudinally in mountains, appear to have been formed by compression and not tension, and because instead of cutting across older structures they conform to the regional structures and have mountains of different types on either side. Volcanism is not an important feature of these. They appear to be associated with compressional mountain-building and not with rifting and continental drift.

Continental Grabens Springing from Secondary Mountains

The Rhine graben, which abuts against the Alps at one end, extends across the covered shield of Europe. Minor volcanism has occurred in places along it (De Sitter 1964).

Similarly located with respect to the Puna block of the Andes is the Chiquitos graben in Bolivia (Ahlfeld and Branisa 1960).

Older examples situated in the same position relative to Appalachian secondary mountains (i.e. folded miogeosynclines) are the Saguenay and Ottawa grabens and the Kentucky River–Rough Creek fault zone. In none of these is volcanism important. All seem to have been formed in part of the compressional process of mountain-building and are not to be connected with rifting and continental drift.

Submarine Trenches with Island Arcs and Primary Mountains

These trenches, which are the deepest in the ocean, lie off many island arcs and chains and off the Andes Mountains in Peru and Chile. While earthquakes show them to be bounded on at least one side by active faults, they have always been held to form a separate category of trenches distinct from grabens, and there seems to be no point in changing this usage.

Ocean Deeps along Fracture Zones

These deeps, of which several have recently been found bounded by great sheer faults on the ocean floors, appear to form a separate if still little-studied type of graben.

Terminations of Rifts

At several places, the mid-ocean ridges or great rifts reach continents or terminate. These places are of particular interest.

San Andreas Fault

If the East Pacific Rise is an expanding rift, it seems entirely logical that it should end at the mouth of the Gulf of California in a right-handed transcurrent fault—the San Andreas fault. It seems unneccessary, and supporting evidence is too little, to suppose that the rift continues up the coast to Alaska (Menard 1960).

Chilean Faults

As a result of the work of St. Amand (1961) a series of large right-handed transcurrent faults is now known to parallel the coast of Chile. This appears to provide the same type of ending as in California and is due to expansion of the southern branch of the East Pacific Rise.

Somalia Coast Fault

B. H. Baker pointed out to me that the coast of Kenya and Somalia is straight and probably faulted. The southern end of this fault extends into a graben in Tanganyika, while the northern part crosses the Carlsberg ridge and extends along the coast of southeastern Arabia. If the Carlsberg ridge has been expanding to form the Arabian Sea, then this fault could have formed its terminus from its beginning to Miocene time, when the Arabian Gulf and Red Sea started to form.

The Jordan Valley Fault

Between Upper Eocene and Lower Miocene time, the Arabian Gulf and Red Sea started to open. Girdler has referred to this as a rotation, but instead of a slight rotation a northward movement along the Jordan Valley is a possible explanation. That this did occur is supported by field evidence.

Dixey (1956, p. 38) summarizes this as follows: "The Dead Sea and Bekaa (Lebanon) faulted and folded structures appear to mark the transition from the East African Rift System to the more complicated rift conditions of the north, showing the normal block faulting of the one becoming involved in the oblique fold and thrust structures of the other." As at the southern end of the African rifts, movements began in Jurassic time, as they did in the northern extension of the Jordan Valley rift towards Turkey.

It is tempting to suppose that the Carlsberg rift ended formerly at the Somalia fault and that it broke through the Somalia fault terminus in Lower Miocene or earlier times and started to open the Arabian Gulf and Red Sea by a rift that again ended on a transcurrent fault in the Jordan Valley. There is no evidence of such transcurrent motion in the Gulf of Suez.

The Arctic Sea Terminus

As is well known, if the two sides of the Atlantic Ocean separated by rifting, the movements involved a rotation through 15° about a fulcrum at the New Siberian Islands. Compression on the opposite side of the fulcrum has been held to have caused the compression of the Verkhoyansk Mountains (Wilson 1963).

Speculation about what happened to Greenland during this movement gives rise to at least three possible views. Previously, the writer has followed

Wegener and Taylor in believing that the opening of Baffin Bay was accompanied by transcurrent faulting of Greenland and Ellesmere Island. A second suggestion is based on an observation of De Geer (1926)—pointed out by Wegmann (1948)—that a line having the form of a small circle passes from northern Norway along the northern border of the Scandic Sea, through the Nansen Sill between Spitsbergen and Greenland, and thence along the straight continental margin to the Beaufort Sea off Alaska. Taylor and Du Toit and Wegmann considered that this might be a fault.

A third suggestion combines the two previous ones and assumes that two faults exist and were once active. According to this reconstruction, it is easy to see why the mid-Atlantic ridge from Iceland through Jan Mayen Island does not pass to the Nansen Sill, but rather to the continental margin at Bear Island. It is believed that this is a refinement of Heezen and Ewing's reconstruction. The line of earthquake epicentres follows De Geer's line because it is an active transcurrent fault, just as earthquakes continue from the East Pacific Rise along the San Andreas fault.

Figure 2 (modified from Wegmann) shows the location of these supposed faults. The opening of these faults and of the Atlantic Ocean would have moved Spitsbergen away from northeast Ellesmere Island. The geology of the former as described by Harland (1960) bears only a general similarity to that of the latter as described by Christie (1964), but Harland (private communication) says that more recent work shows that there is a great similarity in stratigraphy.

On the other hand, the main tectonic and intrusive events are of identical age in the two islands and the intrusives are of similar composition. In Spitzbergen granites were intruded between Lower Ordovician and Devonian times, while in Ellesmere Island Christie reports granitic detritus in the Middle and Upper Ordovician. In both islands a major mountain-building episode took place between Middle Devonian and Mississippian time and is referred to as being "mainly Frasnian" in each case. In both islands basic dykes and sills cut strata of Lower Cretaceous age and are overlain by Palaeocene rocks. Blackadar (1964) has commented that "the average analyses for Spitsbergen diabase and the rocks of the Queen Elizabeth Islands appear to be very similar; both are high in combined iron oxides and low in MgO and CeO," and he noted that they differed from the Thulean igneous suites of similar age in Greenland.

During the Tertiary both islands were subject to folding, faulting, and uplift. In both cases this Alpine disturbance has proved difficult to date precisely and to disentangle from the parallel Caledonian structures. It is thus evident that the history of the islands is similar. The Cretaceous intrusives may have been emplaced during the rifting of the Atlantic Ocean.

Older Transcurrent Faults

One of the most conspicuous of these is the great fault along the south side of Great Slave Lake first mapped by Stockwell (1936). It separates

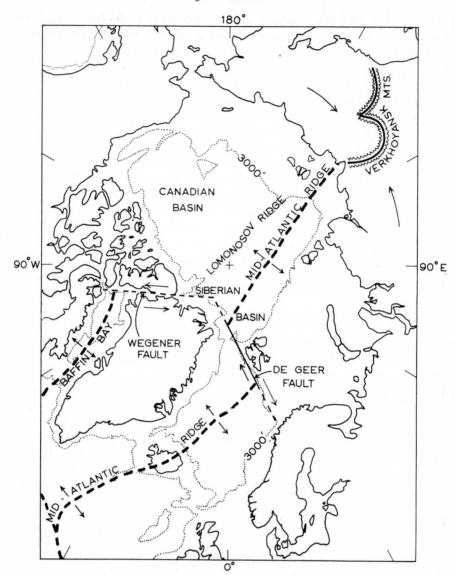

FIGURE 2. Map of the North Atlantic showing the Geer and Wegener faults and the mid-ocean ridge which bifurcates and was offset by these faults.

Precambrian metamorphic rocks of different ages. Aeromagnetic maps and the investigations of oil companies have shown that it continues under Palaeozoic cover as far as the mountains. Far to the east along the same strike, air photographs show a well-marked fault zone striking inland from the west side of Hudson Bay along the south shore of Wager Bay. The two faults appear to line up, but it has proved impossible to establish a connection because of the extent of cover by later sandstones and glacial drift.

A fault zone about which more speculation is possible is the Great Glen fault across Scotland and its possible extensions. Northward it has not been reported beyond the Shetland Islands, but its former connection with the Cabot fault zone in the Atlantic provinces and New England states has been suggested (Wilson 1962). South of Rhode Island the fault disappears beneath the sea, but P. B. King (1964) has recently pointed out that the Brevard schist zone dividing the Blue Ridge and Piedmont provinces is probably a large transcurrent fault and that it has approximately the same strike and position in the Appalachians as would a continuation of the Cabot fault, although no connection has been traced between them.

It may be that the two fault systems do not connect. If they do, the connection may follow the curves of the mountain, but it also may be that both faults strike out to the Atlantic and that there is a gap between them.

In this connection it is interesting to note that Sougy (1962) has recently suggested that there are Appalachian structures in northeastern Africa, and Emile Rod (1962) has pointed out that they contain large transcurrent faults. Harland (private communication) has referred to evidence of transcurrent faulting in the Shetland Islands and in Spitsbergen and to their possible submarine connection with the Great Glen faults. Could it be that the Brevard, northwest Africa, Cabot, Great Glen, Shetland, and Spitsbergen faults are all one. If so, they were probably formed in Late Devonian and Early Mississippian time as the protocontinents of Europe, North America, Africa, and possibly South America came together. King (1964, p. 12) has asked: "Why should there be a great strike-slip fault, parallel to the grain of the rocks, in the midst of a deformed mountain belt?" Compressional forces that formed the mountains would cause faults striking at an angle across the mountains. On the other hand, if three or four continents had converged, is it not reasonable to suppose that some lateral adjustment might have occurred and might it not often have taken place at the edge of the old continental block, which is at the outer margin of the uplifted Precambrian Blue Ridge of the Appalachians and Long Range of Newfoundland?

ASEISMIC, LATERAL SUBMARINE RIDGES

In an earlier paper the view has been expressed that some places on the mid-ocean ridges have been more abundant sources of lava than others (Wilson, 1965). It is evident that at least from the Miocene to the present Iceland has been a site of numerous volcanoes. If Greenland spread away from Scotland starting in the Cretaceous period and if Iceland had been a source of lava throughout that time, then the ridge joining these three localities would be a natural consequence and its existence shows how to fit Greenland to Europe, for the two ends of the ridge would have had to be together. It is significant to note on a globe that this ridge is parallel to the De Geer fault.

In the same way another ridge joins Baffin Island to west Greenland across Baffin Bay. The volcanics of Upper Cretaceous to Eocene age in west Greenland are well known (Munck and Noe-Nygaard 1957). In the summer of 1964 the writer and D. B. Clarke investigated the lavas on Baffin Island, the existence of which had been reported but which had not been studied. Specimens of fossil flora collected by Clarke have been identified by W. A. Bell as lying within the same range in time as the fossils in west Greenland (Wilson and Clarke, 1965). This ridge is also parallel to a transcurrent fault, that between Greenland and Ellesmere Island.

Other such ridges are the Rio Grande and Walvis ridges joining Tristan da Cunha to South America and Africa, respectively, and some of the ridges in the Indian Ocean and the shorter ridge in the Atlantic Ocean through the Azores and Ascension Island.

Some Tentative Rules Governing Continental Drift

1. Compression of great but unmeasured amount may take place along active primary mountains. Some rotation of the sides may accompany compression.

2. Shearing may take place along the same systems or on independent transcurrent fault zones.

3. Expansion may occur at mid-ocean ridges and may be accompanied by some rotation of the sides.

4. Neither continents nor ocean floors have undergone random deformation. All distortion and movement can be traced to one of the above zones of fracture.

5. Mid-ocean ridges usually end in large transcurrent faults. They may pinch out and their place be taken by compression ranges beyond the fulcrum (e.g. the Arctic Mid-Ocean ridge changing to the Verkhoyansk range).

6. Some places in the mantle generate much lava and such places give rise to aseismic ridges. These ridges may show the locus of movement of the crust past such sources (Hawaiian Islands).

7. Where two aseismic ridges lead either way from a volcanic island on a mid-ocean ridge to opposite continents, the ends of the ridges were once in contact (Walvis and Rio Grande ridges).

References

Ahlfeld, F. and Branisa, L. (1960). Geologia de Bolivia. La Paz, Bolivia: Inst. Boliviano del Petroleo, Editorial Don Bosco.

Blackadar, R. G. (1964). Basic intrusions of the Queen Elizabeth Islands, District of Franklin, Canada. Geol. Surv. Can., Bull. 97.

Carey, S. W. (1958). The tectonic approach to continental drift. *In* Continental Drift, a Symposium. Hobart Tasmania: Geology Dept., Univ. of Tasmania.

Christie, R. L. (1964). Geological reconnaissance of Northeastern Ellesmere Island, District of Franklin, Canada. Geol. Surv. Can., Mem. 331.

De Geer, G. (1926). Om de geografiske hurredproblemen i nordpolsomrädet. Ymer, *46*: 133–145.

DE SITTER, L. U. (1964). Structural Geology, 2nd ed. New York: McGraw-Hill Book Co. Inc.

DIETZ, ROBERT S. (1962). Ocean-basin evolution by sea-floor spreading. In Continental Drift, edited by S. K. Runcorn, pp. 289–298. New York and London: Academic Press.

DIXEY, F. (1956). The East African rift system. Colonial Geol. and Min. Resources, Bull. Suppl. no. 1, pp. 1–71.

DRAKE, C. L. and GIRDLER, R. W. (1964). A geophysical study of the Red Sea. Geophys. J., 8: 473–495.

FORTIER, Y. O. and MORLEY, L. W. (1956). Geological unity of the Arctic Islands. Trans. Roy. Soc. Can., Ser. 3, Can. Comm. on Oceanogr., 50: 3–12.

GEZE, B. (1953). Les volcans du Cameroun occidental. Bull. Volc., ser. 2, 13: 63–92.

GIRDLER, R. W. (1963). Geophysical studies of rift valleys. Phys. and Chem. of the Earth, 5: 122–156.

HARLAND, W. B. (1960). An outline structural history of Spitsbergen. Geol. of the Arctic, 1: 68–132.

HEEZEN, B. C. and EWING, M. (1960). The mid-oceanic ridge and its extension through the Arctic Basin. Geol. of the Arctic, 1: 622–642.

HESS, H. H. (1962). History of ocean basins. In Petrologic Studies: A Volume to Honor A. F. Buddington, edited by A. E. J. Engel, H. L. James, and B. L. Leonard, pp. 599–620. New York: Geol. Soc. Amer.

HILLS, E. S. (1963). Elements of Structural Geology. London: Methuen and Co., Ltd.

HOLMES, A. (1931). Radioactivity and Earth Movements. Trans. Geol. Soc. Glasgow, 18: 559–606.

HOLTEDAHL, O. (1950). Supposed marginal fault lines in the shelf area off some high northern lands. Bull. Geol. Soc. Amer., 61: 493–500.

JACOBS, J. A., RUSSELL, R. D., and WILSON, J. TUZO (1959). Physics and Geology. New York: McGraw-Hill Book Co. Inc.

KING, P. B. (1964). Further thoughts on the tectonic framework of southeastern United States. Virginia Polytechnical Inst., Dept. Geol. Sci., Mem. 1, pp. 5–31.

MENARD, H. W. (1960). The East Pacific rise. Science, 132: 1737–1746.

MESNER, J. C. and WOOLRIDGE, L. C. P. (1964). Maramhão Paleozoic basin and Cretaceous coastal basins, North Brazil. Bull. Amer. Assoc. Petrol. Geol., 48, 1475–1512.

MUNCK, S. and NOE-NYGAARD, A. (1957). Age determination of the various stages of the Tertiary volcanism in the West Greenland basalt province. 20th Internat. Geol. Congr., Mexico, Sect. 1, pp. 247–256.

OLIVEIRA, A. I. (1951). Notas sobre a fossa tectónica do Marajo. Eng. Min. e Met. Rio de Janeiro, 16 (no. 93): 201–202.

ROD, EMILE (1962). Geological note on fault pattern, northwest corner of Sahara shield. Bull. Amer. Assoc. Petrol. Geol., 46: 529.

ST. AMAND, P. (1961). Los Terremotos de Mayo, Chile, 1960. Michelson Lab., U.S. Naval Ord. Test Station, N.O.T.S., T.P. 2701, China Lake, Calif., U.S.A.

SOUGY, J. (1962). West African fold belt. Bull. Geol. Soc. Amer., 73: 871–876.

STOCKWELL, C. (1936). Eastern portion of Great Slave Lake. Geol. Surv. Can., Maps 377A and 378A.

TAYLOR, E. F. (1952). Geology and oil fields of Brazil. Bull. Amer. Assoc. Petrol. Geol., 36: 1613–1626.

UMBGROVE, J. H. F. (1947). The Pulse of the Earth, 2nd ed. The Hague: Martinus Frijhoff.

WALKER, G. P. L. (1960). Zeolite zones and dike distribution. J. Geol., 48: 515–528.

WEGMAN, C. E. (1948). Geological tests of the hypothesis of continental drift in the Arctic regions. Medd. om Grønland, 144 (no. 7): 1–48.

WILSON, J. TUZO (1962). Some further evidence in support of the Cabot fault. Trans. Roy. Soc. Can., Ser. 3, Sec. III, 56: 31–36.

——— (1963). Hypothesis of earth's behavior. Nature, 198: 925–929.

——— (1965). Evidence from ocean islands suggesting movement in the earth. Symposium on Continental Drift, 1964. Phil. Trans. Roy. Soc. (London), 258: 145–167.

WILSON, J. T. and CLARK, D. B. (1965). Geological expedition to Capes Dyer and Searle, Baffin Island, Canada. Nature, 205: 349–350.

MANTLE PROPERTIES AND CONTINENTAL DRIFT

Gordon J. F. MacDonald

THE MUCH-DEBATED HYPOTHESIS of continental drift seems to provide an elegant and simple solution to many questions concerning the evolution of the earth's crust. Advocates of the theory affirm its ability to explain puzzling problems of tectonics, ice ages, animal and plant migration, and palaeomagnetism. However, while the hypothesis of continental drift is supposed to solve many problems connected with the surface of the earth, it also raises substantial questions about the upper mantle.

Geophysical studies pose objections of two kinds to the theory of continental drift. The first class of objections rests on the contradictions created by supposing that continental blocks have travelled over large horizontal distances. These objections do not involve the mechanism driving continental drift, but rest solely on the effects of moving continents on the mantle structure. The second class of objections depends on the proposed mechanism for continental drift. In the past, rotational, tidal, and gravitational forces have been invoked, while in more recent times the efficacy of convection currents has been emphasized. Straightforward calculations of the forces involved apparently rule out all mechanisms but that of convection (Jeffreys 1959). The known properties of the mantle can be compared with those required if convection currents are to move continental masses.

The present discussion is concerned with two questions. Is the upper-mantle structure compatible with continental drift? In the following section, I review the evidence bearing on the large-scale structure of the upper mantle and suggest that major contradictions arise if thin continental blocks are supposed to have sailed over the earth's surface. The second question is concerned with the mechanical properties of the earth's mantle. Are these properties compatible with the suggested mechanism of convection? New and important evidence secured from observations of earth satellites suggests that the mechanical properties of the earth may be far more complicated than those envisaged by proponents of the convection theory.

CONTINENT STRUCTURE IN THE UPPER MANTLE OF THE EARTH

The structures of continents and oceans differ greatly at and near the surface. Does this difference end at the Mohorovicic discontinuity, or at some level of compensation (about 40–100 km), or do the differences extend to much greater depths? Recent evidence derived from gravity, heat flow, and seismological observations suggests that the differences are not restricted to upper layers, but extend to depths of several hundred kilometres (Mac-Donald 1963, 1964).

It has long been known that, on the average, the gravitation field over continents equals that over oceans, and, consequently, that the mass per unit area is the same beneath water and land, despite great differences in surface density. New observations from satellites, however, establish that there are large-scale variations in the gravity field. The observed field can be compared with that expected for a fluid earth; this comparison yields residuals with magnitudes much greater than can be accounted for by errors in observation and interpretation (Munk and MacDonald 1960a). Part of the observed deviation could arise from an isostatically compensated crust. When a calculation of the external potential of an isostatically compensated crust is carried out, it is found that, for the low-order harmonics, the gravity anomalies expected for the crust are small compared with the observed anomalies, and are of opposite sign. Thus, there must exist inhomogeneities in the mantle mass distribution that are correlated with continent–ocean structure, but in the sense opposite to that expected from ordinary isostasy.

In current treatments of isostasy, mass is calculated above a certain level, usually about 30 to 40 km; the columns under oceans and under continents are found to have approximately the same mass, provided reasonable values are assigned to the densities of the constituent materials (Worzel and Shurbet 1954; Hess 1962). Implicit in such calculations is the assumption that the mantle is horizontally homogeneous below a given level. Unless all crustal material under continents is extracted from a very thin layer of the mantle, this assumption must be invalid. The difference in chemical composition of the continental and oceanic crust requires a difference in chemical composition extending over some depth within the mantle. If the continental material is derived in part from the oceanic mantle, then, in order to maintain the average equality of mass per unit area over continents and oceans, there must be a compensating transfer of continental mantle material to oceanic mantle. Both heat-flow and gravity observations deny this last hypothesis.

Observations of heat flow imply deep-seated differences between continents and oceans, similar to those derived from gravity observations. Lee and MacDonald (1963) analysed over 900 measurements of surface heat flow. The global mean is 63.9 ± 3.4 erg cm^{-2} sec^{-1}.* The average over continents is 68.9 erg cm^{-2} sec^{-1}, while the average over oceans is 62.0 erg cm^{-2} sec^{-1}. The averages represent 92 continental measurements and 665 oceanic measurements. The differences between continents and oceans are not significant, and this analysis supports the contention of Bullard (1954)

*[Editor's note: 42 erg cm^{-2} sec^{-1} corresponds approximately to 1 microcal cm^{-2} sec^{-1}.]

and Revelle and Maxwell (1952) that the heat flow from ocean bottoms approximately equals the heat flow through the continents.

The heat flow represents an unknown sampling of the various means by which heat has been produced within the earth in the past. The principal contributors are the heat produced by the radioactive decay of elements, the heat resulting from the conversion of gravitational energy, and the heat produced by tidal friction. Suppose that radioactivity is the principal heat source. MacDonald (1963) estimates that somewhere between 10 and 40 erg cm^{-2} sec^{-1} of heat is flowing into the crust from the mantle, with most analyses favouring the lower figure, although the estimation of the heat sources within continental masses is a notoriously hazardous procedure. A surface flux in oceanic regions of 62 erg cm^{-2} sec^{-1} implies that between 56 and 59 erg cm^{-2} sec^{-1} must be flowing from the interior into the region above 40 km. The difference in flux between continents and oceans at a depth of 40 km is then between 16 and 49 erg cm^{-2} sec^{-1}. Even when we take the extreme limits of error in the values of heat production and heat flow as a basis of calculation, we find a considerable difference in the amounts of heat flowing into the crust beneath the land and sea. The difference in outward heat flow at a depth of 40 km implies deep-seated differences in temperature under continents and oceans. These, in turn, will produce inequalities in density if the materials underlying the continents and oceans are identical in composition and phase. The perturbation of the density field resulting from varying thermal conditions must be taken into account in a proper treatment of isostasy.

Heat flow observations, like those of gravity, require deep-seated differences between continents and oceans. This conclusion rests on an estimate of the concentration of radioactive elements within the continental crust. If the continental crust has the average composition of a basalt, then the above constraint on the mantle structure loses much of its force.

As yet, studies of the propagation of body and surface waves do not yield a detailed picture of the difference between the continental and oceanic mantle. However, there are several important indications that the mantle under the ocean does indeed differ from that under continents, and there may be variations under continents related to the continental structure. The distribution of earthquake foci provides additional indirect evidence that there are major differences in continental and oceanic structures extending to a depth of several hundred kilometres.

Classical distributions of elastic wave velocity in the mantle, as determined by Jeffreys (1939) and Gutenberg and Richter (1935, 1936), deviate principally in the upper 500 km of the mantle. At greater depths, the two distributions are very similar. Evidence that the mantle at depths greater than 500–1000 km is homogeneous on a large scale and can be described by a radial velocity distribution comes from a study of the free oscillations. The close agreement obtained by various workers (Pekeris *et al.* 1961; Mac-Donald and Ness 1961) between observed and calculated low-order spheroidal and toroidal oscillations clearly indicates that, on the average, the deep mantle can be described by velocity distributions that are a function of depth alone. However, the low-order oscillations are not sensitive to variations in mantle properties at shallow depths.

The principal seismic evidence for a distinction between continents and oceans within the mantle comes from studies of surface waves. Dorman *et al.* (1960) show that the low-velocity zone is present at a depth between 50 and 250 km under the ocean and has a minimum velocity of about 4.3 km sec^{-1}. In contrast, Dorman finds that the low-velocity zone is deeper under continents and the minimum velocity is greater than under oceans. Sutton *et al.* (1960) obtained similar results. Comparable results have been obtained with Love wave dispersion curves by Sykes *et al.* (1962) and Kovach and Anderson (1962). Brune and Dorman (1963) have carried out a detailed study of the propagation of surface waves across strictly continental paths, where the paths traverse predominantly Precambrian shield areas. The low-velocity zone is found to be present between 120 and approximately 300 km, with a minimum velocity of 4.5 km sec^{-1}, a velocity which is substantially greater than that found in oceanic regions.

The interpretation of the surface-wave dispersion data is not unique. Various combinations of velocity distributions yield good agreement with observations. However, it appears that the recent interpretations all lead to the conclusion that continents and oceans do differ, at least in the upper 300 km. The difference is principally in the depth of the low-velocity zone and the minimum velocity within that zone. In general, this minimum velocity is lower under oceans than under continents. If the low-velocity zone is due primarily to a competition between the temperature and pressure effects, then the lower minimum velocity under oceans is consistent with the hypothesis that the temperature under oceans is higher than that under continents, as is required by consideration of heat flow.

It has long been known that the principal earthquake zones are at continent-ocean interfaces. No earthquake foci have been found below approximately 720 km, and below approximately 650 km, the frequency of earthquakes decreases rapidly (Gutenberg and Richter 1954, 1956a, b). The association of earthquake foci with continental borders is particularly marked for those earthquakes that have foci at a depth greater than 300 km. The interpretation of the association of earthquake zones with continental borders and the limitation of earthquakes to the upper 700 km of the earth depend on the mechanism by which earthquakes are generated. MacDonald (1963) argues that the difference in heat source distribution between continents and oceans is primarily responsible for the concentration of earthquake zones along young continent–ocean boundaries. While the differential thermal loss may not contribute sufficient strain energy for large earthquakes, this mechanism provides a means of obtaining faults with vertical displacements along continental borders. These zones of weakness are then the loci of energy release due to elastic distortion not directly associated with differential heat production and loss. The limitation of earthquakes to the region in the upper 700 km of the earth can be interpreted either in terms of a first-order change in the mechanical properties of the material at this depth, or of the vanishing of the effects of differential thermal losses in the regions below 700 km. Thus, if continents are formed by the upward concentration of mantle material, and if this process has affected the upper 700 km of the mantle, then thermal stresses will be associated with the continent–ocean boundaries down to depths of the order of 700 km. Below this depth, radioactive sources are horizontally homogeneous and thermal stresses due to differential thermal losses do not develop. The association of earthquake zones with continental borders, plus the depth limitation, can be interpreted in terms of a continental structure extending to at least 500 km. This conclusion is concordant with conclusions derived from heat flow, gravity, and direct seismic observations. The extension of differences between the present continent–ocean structure to depth implies that any theory of continental drift must provide a mechanism by which this deep structure is maintained intact. The proposed deep structure of continents is incompatible with the notion that thin continental blocks sail on a viscous substrate, pushed along by near-surface convection currents.

MECHANICAL PROPERTIES OF THE MANTLE

The most plausible mechanism for providing the motive force for continental drift is that of thermally driven convection. The development of a theory of convection within the mantle requires the description of the mechanical properties of the mantle material. Since data on the long-term response of mantle material to stress differences are quite limited, only primitive models of the mechanical response of the mantle can be constructed.

Among the models for the mechanical behaviour of the mantle we have the following:

1. The mantle behaves as an elastic solid below a critical yield stress. At stresses above the critical yield stress, material fractures or ruptures, with consequent plastic flow.

2. The material in the mantle can be considered as an elastoviscous material. For rapid, high-frequency excitation, the mantle behaves as an elastic solid, while for low-frequency deformations, it behaves as a viscous fluid. A critical property is that there is no finite stress that must be exceeded prior to permanent deformation.

3. Long-term deformation follows the laws of creep. There is a finite creep strength that must be exceeded before permanent deformation takes place. The flow and stress differences above that specified by the creep strength are determined by a non-Newtonian viscosity.

Both the first and third models involve the non-linear response of material and, therefore, have received little attention from the mathematically minded geophysicist. On the other hand, the elastoviscous model yields readily to theoretical treatment, particularly since many of the results from elasticity can be carried over with only minor modifications.

Evidence relating to the response of the mantle to small stress deformations is of three kinds:

1. Munk and MacDonald (1960*b*) show that the present figure of the earth deviates from that of an equilibrium fluid in the sense expected for a rotationally decelerating earth. The equatorial bulge is too large and corresponds to an equilibrium bulge appropriate for the rate of rotation some 10^7 years ago. This observation is appropriate to discussions of continental drift, since it involves a long time-scale and is of large amplitude (the equilibrium flattening is $1/298.23$, while the flattening of an equivalent rotating fluid is $1/299.8$).

2. Numerous studies on the rebound of glaciated areas in Fenno-Scandia (Kääriäinen 1953; Niskanen 1948) provide additional evidence on the mechanical properties of the mantle.

3. More recently, a detailed study of the uplift of Pleistocene Lake Bonneville has been presented by Crittenden (1963). As for the Pleistocene uplift, the time-scale is of the order of 5×10^3 years, while dimensions are an order of magnitude less than those of continental glaciation.

The change in the earth's figure is due to a change in the centrifugal potential, while the Lake Bonneville and Fenno-Scandian uplifts result from a change in the surface load. The relation between these deformations is most easily described in terms of Love numbers and operators (Munk and MacDonald 1960*b*). We consider the response of the earth to a disturbing potential U of degree two; the centrifugal force arising from rotation can be written as the gradient of such a potential U. The earth is deformed as a result of the finite elasticity, and the additional gravitational potential at the displaced surface arising solely from the redistribution of mass is $k_2 U$, where k_2 is the dimensionless Love number. Observation of bodily tides, Chandler wobble, etc. can be used to obtain a value of k_2.

Kelvin has shown that for an incompressible homogeneous sphere of rigidity μ', density ρ, surface gravity g, and radius a, the Love number k_2 is

(1)
$$k_2 = \frac{3/2}{1 + \mu},$$

where

$$\mu = \frac{19}{2} \frac{\mu'}{\rho g a}.$$

The dimensionless rigidity μ can be replaced by a value that yields a k_2 in agreement with the observations. Thus, the substitution of $\mu = 2.3$ takes into account the radial variations of density and elasticity.

The Love number k_2 defined by (1) is appropriate when considering changes in the earth's rotation. A surface load has two effects. There is a potential arising from the gravitational attraction of the load, and there is stress, which depresses the surface. Munk and MacDonald show that the Love number k_2' due to the surface load is

(2)
$$k_2' = -\tfrac{2}{3} k_2.$$

In the general case of an external potential of degree n, the appropriate value for k_n is

$$(3) \qquad k_n = \frac{3/2}{n-1} \frac{1}{1+\mu N},$$

where

$$N = \frac{2(2n^2 + 4n + 3)}{19n},$$

and for a load we have

$$(4) \qquad k_n' = -\frac{1}{1+\mu N}.$$

In a Maxwellian, or elastoviscous, body, the total rate of deformation is written as the sum of an elastic and viscous term. In the one-dimensional case, this is

$$(5) \qquad \frac{1}{s}\frac{ds}{dt} = \frac{1}{2\mu'} + \frac{d}{dt}(\sigma_{\text{elastic}}) + \frac{1}{2\eta}(\sigma_{\text{elastic}}),$$

where ds/dt is the actual rate at which two points move apart, η is the dynamic viscosity, and σ_{elastic} is the elastic stress. Once the elastic problem has been solved, the solution for the Maxwell body can be found by replacing the dimensionless rigidity μ (see equation 1) by

$$(6) \qquad \hat{\mu} = \frac{\mu D}{D + \tau^{-1}}$$

(Jeffreys 1959). $\tau = \eta'/\mu'$ is the characteristic time constant and D is the differential time operator. The load Love number for a Maxwell earth becomes

$$(7) \qquad \hat{k}_n' = -\frac{1}{1+N\mu}.$$

The formalism sketched in equations (1) through (7) can be used to determine the time history of a load suddenly applied at time zero. That history is given by

$$(1 + k_n')H(t) = \frac{N\mu}{1+N\mu}\frac{D}{D+\gamma_n}H(t)$$

$$= \frac{N\mu}{1+N\mu}e^{-\gamma_n t},$$

where H is the Heaviside step function and γ_n^{-1} is the compensation time, which is given by

$$(9) \qquad \gamma_n^{-1} = (1 + N\mu)\tau.$$

The factor $N\mu/(1 + N\mu)$ accounts for the immediate effects due to elastic deformation.

The uplift in Lake Bonneville has a characteristic wavelength of about 200 km, which corresponds to an n of about 200. The compensation time is about 4000 years (Crittenden 1963), so that the corresponding time constant τ is

$$(10) \qquad \tau = \frac{1.3 \times 10^{11}}{[1 + 24.1\,(2.3)]} = 2.3 \times 10^9 \text{ sec.}$$

The characteristic time τ is related to the viscosity and rigidity by

$$(11) \qquad \tau = \eta'/\mu',$$

so that

$$(12) \qquad \eta' = \mu'\tau = 2.3 \times 10^9 \mu'.$$

A rigidity of 8.3×10^{11} dyne cm^{-2}, consistent with a value of μ of 2.31, yields a dynamic viscosity of 1.9×10^{21} dyne sec cm^{-2}.

A similar calculation can be carried out for the Fenno-Scandian uplift. The length scale is of the order of 2000 km, corresponding to an n of 20. The time-scale is of the order of 5000 years. The resulting dynamic viscosity is 2.3×10^{22} dyne sec cm^{-2}. The large-scale deformation yields a higher value for the viscosity.

For the case of a change in the external potential due to the slowing down of the earth, the relationship between the characteristic time τ and the time constant γ_2^{-1} is

$$(13) \qquad \gamma_2^{-1} = (1 + \mu)\tau.$$

For a time constant of 10^7 years, the dynamic viscosity corresponding to a rigidity of 8.3×10^{11} dyne cm^{-2} is 8.0×10^{25} dyne sec cm^{-2}.

The discrepancy in the values of viscosity derived from these three observations results either from a variation of the anelastic properties within the earth or the inappropriateness of the elastoviscous model. In the first interpretation, the consistent association of a higher viscosity with a low value of n indicates that, on the average, the mantle is quite viscous, but that there may be a near-surface layer of low viscosity (Takeuchi 1963). This interpretation meets with difficulty in that one must suppose that all small-scale deviations from isostasy, such as the association of large gravity anomalies with ancient mountain chains, must be maintained by some dynamic process (Munk and MacDonald 1960b).

An alternative interpretation is that mantle material undergoes creep at low stress differences. Creep is characterized by creep strength, i.e., some stress difference that must be exceeded before permanent deformation can take place. At a fixed stress above the creep strength, there is a slow replacement of elastic strain by plastic strain at constant total strain. In this region, the rate of deformation depends in a complex fashion on the remaining elastic strain. The available data on creep in geologically important materials are still limited (Heard 1960, 1963). In a creep model for the mantle, at least two parameters are required to describe the mechanical behaviour of the material. The first parameter is the creep strength, and the second is the complex function of the elastic strain. Both of these parameters are expected to be functions of the radius within the mantle.

An important characteristic of creep is that the creep rate at a given stress usually doubles or trebles for each 10° C rise in temperature. This dependence of the creep strength and rate of creep on temperature is of great importance in considering the mechanical behaviour of mantle material if a creep model is appropriate.

Rough estimates of the stress differences associated with the Pleistocene Lake Bonneville, Fenno-Scandian uplift, and the rotational deformation of the earth are 5 bars, 50 bars, and 200 bars, respectively (Crittenden 1963; Munk and MacDonald 1960b; Kaula 1963). This would suggest that the creep strength varies with radius and the uppermost part of the mantle has a lower creep strength than the deep mantle.

The existence of a region within the mantle in which the creep strength of viscosity is a minimum, separating the continent–ocean structure from the deeper mantle, poses severe difficulties with the convection theory of continental drift. This region would effectively decouple the continents and oceans from the deeper mantle. In addition, the higher viscosity or greater creep strength implied for the lower mantle places severe constraints on convection in this region. It would appear that a simple, constant-viscosity model for the mantle is inconsistent with observations. The implied radial variations in mechanical properties present additional difficulties to the convection theory for continental drift.

REFERENCES

BRUNE, J. and DORMAN, J. (1963). Seismic waves and earth structure in the Canadian Shield. Bull. Seismol. Soc. Amer., 53: 167–210.

BULLARD, E. C. (1954). The flow of heat through the floor of the Atlantic Ocean. Proc. Roy. Soc. (London), Ser. A, 222: 408–429.

CRITTENDEN, M. (1963). Effective viscosity of the earth derived from isostatic loading of Pleistocene Lake Bonneville. J. Geophys. Res., 68: 5517–5530.

DORMAN, J. EWING, M., and OLIVER, J. (1960). Study of shear velocity distribution in the upper mantle by Rayleigh waves. Bull. Seismol. Soc. Amer., 50: 87–115.

GUTENBERG, B. and RICHTER, C. F. (1935). On seismic waves (second paper). Gerlands Beitr. Geophys., 45: 280–360.

——— (1936). On seismic waves (third paper). Gerlands Beitr. Geophys., 47: 73–131.

——— (1954). Seismicity of the Earth and Associated Phenomena. Princeton, N.J.: Princeton Univ. Press.

——— (1956a). Magnitude and energy of earthquakes. Ann. Geophys., 9: 1–15.

——— (1956b). Earthquake magnitude, intensity, energy, and acceleration (second paper). Bull. Seismol. Soc. Amer., 46: 105–145.

HEARD, H. C. (1960). Transition from middle fracture to ductile flow in Solenhofen limestone as a function of temperature, confining pressure, and interstitial fluid pressure. Geol. Soc. Amer., Mem. 79, pp. 193–226.

———— (1963). Effect of large changes in strain rate in the experimental deformation of Yule marble. J. Geol., *71*: 162–195.

Hess, H. H. (1962). History of ocean basins. *In* Petrologic Studies, A Volume to Honor A. F. Buddington, *edited by* A. E. J. Engel, H. L. James, and B. L. Leonard, pp. 599–620. New York: Geol. Soc. Amer.

Jeffreys, H. (1939). The times of PS and SKS and the velocity of P and S. Mon. Not. Roy. Astron. Soc., Geophys. Suppl., *4*: 498–533.

———— (1959). The Earth, 4th ed. London: Cambridge Univ. Press.

Kääriäinen, E. (1953). On the recent uplift of the earth's crust in Finland. Publ. Finnish Geodetic Inst., no. 42.

Kaula, W. M. (1963). Elastic models of the mantle corresponding to variations in the external gravity field. J. Geophys. Res., *68*: 4967–4978.

Kovach, R. and Anderson, D. (1962). Long-period Love waves in a heterogeneous spherical earth. J. Geophys. Res., *67*: 5243–5255.

Lee, W. H. K. and MacDonald, G. J. F. (1963). The global variation of terrestrial heat flow. J. Geophys. Res., *68*: 6481–6492.

MacDonald, G. J. F. (1963). The deep structure of continents. Rev. Geophys., *1*: 587–665.

———— (1964). Dependence of the surface heat flow on the radioactivity of the earth. J. Geophys. Res., *69*: 2933–2946.

MacDonald, G. J. F. and Ness, N. F. (1961). A study of the free oscillations of the earth. J. Geophys. Res., *66*: 1865–1911.

Munk, W. H. and MacDonald, G. J. F. (1960a). Continentality and the gravitational field of the earth. J. Geophys. Res., *65*: 2169–2172.

———— (1960b). Rotation of the Earth. London: Cambridge Univ. Press.

Niskanen, E. (1948). On the viscosity of the earth's interior and crust. Ann. Akad. Sci. Sennicae, no. 15.

Pekeris, C. L., Alterman, Z., and Jarosch, H. (1961). Comparison of theoretical with observed values of the free oscillations of the earth. Proc. Nat. Acad. Sci., U.S., *47*: 91–98.

Revelle, R. and Maxwell, A. E. (1952). The heat flow through the floor of the eastern North Pacific Ocean. Nature, *170*: 199–200.

Sutton, G., Ewing, M., and Major, M. (1960). Rayleigh wave group velocity extrema. Paper presented in 1960 Helsinki Meeting of the International Association of Seismology and Physics of the Earth's Interior.

Sykes, L., Landisman, M., and Saito, Y. (1962). Mantle shear wave velocity determined from oceanic Love and Rayleigh wave dispersion. J. Geophys. Res., *67*: 5257–5271.

Takeuchi, H. (1963). Time-scales of isostatic compensation. J. Geophys. Res., *68*: 2357.

Worzel, J. L. and Shurbet, G. L. (1954). Gravity interpretations from standard oceanic and continental cross-sections. *In* Crust of the Earth, *edited by* A. Poldervaart. Geol. Soc. Am. Spec. Paper 62, pp. 87–100.

THE ROCK MAGNETIC EVIDENCE FOR CONTINENTAL DRIFT

Ernst R. Deutsch

GEOMAGNETISM developed from a study of phenomena known since antiquity, and is one of the oldest branches of geophysics. *Continental drift* has never been observed directly and must be classed as an unproved geological hypothesis. At first sight the two subjects have nothing in common, yet the recent successful application of palaeomagnetism to the continental drift problem illustrates in what an unpredictable manner two seemingly unrelated scientific topics may become linked. In a sense, these topics had a common inspiration in 16th-century navigation, when the widespread use of the compass prompted enquiries into the nature of the earth's magnetic field, leading Gilbert (1600) to demonstrate that the earth behaves as a magnet. By that time seafarers had produced sufficiently accurate maps to show the similarity in the outlines of opposite Atlantic coasts, a phenomenon to which Francis Bacon drew attention in 1620 (Holmes 1965, p. 1197).

Mining compasses reportedly were introduced about 1640 to locate iron ores. Such methods relate *geo*magnetism to *rock* magnetism by measuring anomalies in the earth's field arising from the polarization of ferromagnetic minerals in surface rocks. A plausible mechanism would be induction by the present field, and parallel to it. The fact that some rocks possess *permanent* polarization not necessarily conforming to the acting field was noticed by Humboldt (1797). In 1853 M. Melloni (see Chevallier 1925) found that lava samples, upon cooling from high temperatures, became permanently magnetized in the direction of the earth's field. These discoveries, which led ultimately to palaeomagnetism, are thus over 100 years old, and so is the first published version of continental drift in 1858 by Antonio Snider (Holmes 1965, p. 1197), who had carried Bacon's observation to its logical conclusion by mapping the coalescence of continents along their Atlantic coastlines.

THE PALAEOMAGNETIC METHOD

Continental drift will be defined as the horizontal displacement of parts of the earth's crust relative to each other. The definition suggests nothing about a mechanism, but this is of no concern here: a method provides evidence simply if it can tell whether two portions of the crust have changed their relative positions laterally. Such a method depends upon the existence of a record from which the reality of the displacements, if not their details, may be deduced with the aid of spherical trigonometry.

Nature of the Evidence

Palaeomagnetic interpretations require not only that the rocks exhibit remanent magnetism, but also: (1) that it be determinable whether this remanence is "stable," in the sense that the magnetic components in the rocks have preserved the earth's field direction prevailing at the time of their origin; (2) that the age of the rocks be known, though imprecise dating (say, with uncertainties of one geological period) need not always disqualify rocks from furnishing useful evidence on continental drift; (3) that correlation of magnetization directions in the rocks with the co-ordinates of a uniformly magnetized sphere be permissible, if during the geological past the geomagnetic field has been essentially that of a geocentric dipole. The final step equating these geomagnetic co-ordinates with ancient *geographical* latitudes and meridians is based on a special case of the above assumption, which specifies that for periods longer than a few thousand years the axis of this presumed dipole has always coincided with the spin axis. This is the "axial dipole assumption."

Suppose that the magnetization had been determined in oriented rock samples of comparable age from two sites on different land masses. Even if conditions (1) to (3) can be assumed to apply, rock magnetism is devious in providing clues on continental drift. At the start, one conveniently resolves the hypothetical displacement at each collection site S into three components: rotation of the land mass about S, translation of S along latitude circles, and translation along meridians. The last component is measured by the dip of the magnetization vector, which gives the ancient latitude, while the rotation is given by its azimuth. The component parallel to the latitude is not deducible from the magnetic data, leaving the palaeolongitude of S undefined.

The magnetic data are usually plotted as *pole positions* relative to the collection site S; these are calculated from the azimuth and dip of the remanent magnetization, averaged over all the specimens under study, and the present latitude and longitude of S. A series of pole positions based on successively younger rock formations on the same land mass may be joined by a *polar wandering curve* terminating at the present geographical pole. Finally, one compares the polar wandering curves relative to two land masses, to infer whether they have drifted with respect to each other. However, the fundamental problem of palaeomagnetism lies in assessing the reliability of rock magnetic data and their applicability to problems such as continental drift, rather than in the actual applications. "Reliability" means in effect magnetic stability, which must be established separately in each palaeomagnetic study; whether rock magnetism as such is "applicable" still hinges largely upon the validity of the axial dipole assumption.

Axial Dipole Assumption

The time scale of the secular variation, say 10^3 years, is probably short compared to the time span represented by the samples in a typical collection for magnetic work; an adequate sampling procedure thus tends to eliminate the secular variation from the results. Runcorn (1959), after examining the alternative of axial multipole fields, concluded that their existence, at least during parts of the Palaeozoic and Mesozoic, cannot be reconciled with palaeomagnetic and palaeoclimatological evidence. Blackett, Clegg, and Stubbs (1960) from their analysis consider it unlikely that large multipolar fields could have persisted for periods of the order of 10^8 years. The axial dipole mechanism also fits theoretical models of the origin of the earth's field (Bullard 1949; Runcorn 1954). Palaeomagnetic work by Hospers (1955) and others has demonstrated that the assumption is valid for at least the last million years or so.

Criteria for Confidence

Before one can test the rocks for stability, they must be corrected for post-depositional folding or other reorientation of the strata from which oriented samples were taken for magnetic measurement. While incapable of proof, stability can often be demonstrated with the aid of certain criteria summarized below.

1. *Field tests.* Though restricted in scope, the stability tests due to Graham (1949) can provide strong evidence for deciding whether the observed remanence was acquired before or after a certain geological event, in this case folding of the rock strata or assembly of a conglomerate from older pebbles (Fig. 1).

2. *Laboratory tests.* Thermal and a–c. demagnetization are standard techniques, while d–c. demagnetization, first applied as a stability test by Johnson, Murphy, and Torreson (1948), has found general use in Soviet laboratories (e.g. V. V. Kochegura, in Kalashnikov 1961). All these methods have the double function of confirming the absence of unstable components from an otherwise stable magnetization, or of removing such components where they do exist. Figure 2 shows a striking example of the decisive results that can be achieved by thermal demagnetization.

3. *Dispersion and mean direction of magnetization vectors.* It is customary to surround the computed pole with an oval derived from the statistics of Fisher (1953). Its area is determined by the specified probability that the "true" pole lies inside, and by the number of measurements and their scatter. For most results considered "acceptable" in palaeomagnetism, including the great majority incorporated in Figures 3 and 4, the lengths of the semiaxes of the oval (not shown) are well within 20° of arc. Then a "small" oval suggests relative stability, though care must be taken to prevent unrepresentative weighting of the sample submitted to statistical analysis, which may result in undersized ovals, i.e. in overconfidence (Cox and Doell 1960). Unstable magnetizations tend to be aligned closely with the present field

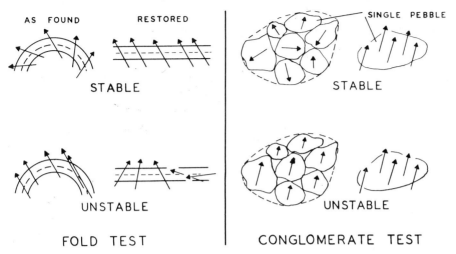

FIGURE 1. Field tests of magnetic stability proposed by J. W. Graham (1949). Arrows indicate the direction of natural remanent magnetism in the rocks. In the fold test it is assumed that the rock strata were originally flat-lying; the test then distinguishes between a magnetization acquired prior to folding ("stable") or after folding ("unstable"). In the conglomerate test it is assumed that the pebbles were removed by erosion from older sedimentary beds; the test distinguishes between a magnetization acquired prior to formation of the conglomerate ("stable") or since that time ("unstable").

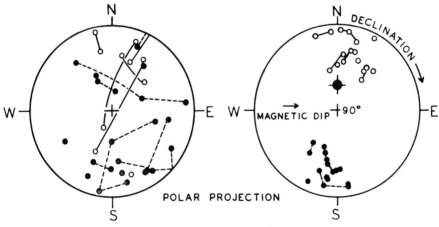

FIGURE 2. Thermal demagnetization of Carboniferous lavas from Scotland, redrawn after Wilson and Everitt (1963), with kind permission of the senior author. Points representing specimens from the same lava flow are joined: o——o, magnetic dip upwards; ●– – –●, downwards; ● present North pole direction (axial dipole). The natural remanent magnetism of several lava flows before heat treatment is depicted at left. On the right are plotted the new magnetic directions observed at temperatures less than about 100° C below the highest Curie point of each specimen. The high-temperature plot shows (1) close agreement between specimens from the same lava; (2) differentiation of the lavas into two distinct sets having directions roughly antiparallel to one another.

direction and could also produce close grouping of the data. Therefore *size* and *location* of the confidence oval must be considered together: generally, some magnetic stability may be diagnosed when the oval is "small" and excludes both the present spin pole and geomagnetic pole ($78\frac{1}{2}°$ N, 69° W). While this is often the case, the magnetization vectors in late Cenozoic rocks typically make small angles with the present spin axis of the earth. In such cases inclusion of the present poles in the confidence ovals may, or may not, signify instability, and other stability criteria must be sought.

4. *Consistency tests*. Agreement between pole positions inferred from contemporaneous rocks at two or more sites in adjacent territory justifies placing increased confidence in each result, provided the confidence ovals exclude the present poles. Intersection of any pair of ovals may be taken roughly as "agreement." Such evidence can be still more convincing when conformable magnetic data are obtained from petrologically different rocks, such as basalts and sandstones, sampled either at different localities or at a single site.

5. *Reversals of magnetization*. For a long time (Brunhes 1906), mutually opposed magnetizations as depicted in Figure 2 have been a familiar phenomenon in rock magnetism. In the middle to late Cenozoic a pattern of "polarity epochs" is now emerging, in which the rocks exhibit alternately "reversed" and "normal" polarity. Accumulating evidence strongly favours the hypothesis that such polarity reversals mostly reflect reversals of the geomagnetic field, though one of the mechanisms of "self-reversal," proposed by Néel (1948), in which the polarity change is caused by a property of the rock itself, has been shown to be responsible in a small number of cases (Nagata, Akimoto, and Uyeda 1952–53; Everitt 1962). The question of polarity reversals and their causes concerns continental drift interpretations only indirectly, since these are based on hypothetical changes in the location and not the polarity of the geomagnetic axis. (A possible exception is Precambrian and Lower Palaeozoic data, where the pole positions often occupy very low latitudes on the present grid, so that the ambiguity in sense may make it difficult to determine a reliable polar wandering path.) Reversals, however, have a strong bearing on the broader problem concerning confidence in the applications of rock magnetism.

First, regardless of cause, one may take the fact that certain rocks are "reversed" as a stability criterion, by reasoning that an unstable magnetization could not oppose the earth's field for a geologically long time. One has an even better criterion when a sequence of rocks of comparable age exhibits "mixed," i.e. alternately "normal" and "reserved" polarity.

Secondly, critics of palaeomagnetism sometimes base their objections on the (incontestable) fact that the origin of the earth's magnetism is not fully understood. Thus MacDonald (1963, p. 611) writes that "it can be argued that the observed reversals in the field suggest a rather short time scale for the field and intervals during which the internal field may not be dipolar." I think MacDonald misinterprets the significance of the term "time scale."

In the Tertiary and early Quaternary a fairly consistent pattern is now emerging: a magnetic study of Icelandic lavas and interbedded sediments led Hospers (1955) to distinguish four time spans since the Miocene in which the rock polarity was reversed, with stable epochs (normal or reversed) persisting on the average for a quarter to half a million years, and the time for switching polarities being of the order of 10,000 years. The latter figure was also inferred by Janovsky (1962) from rock magnetism in western Turkmenia (Khramov 1958), which revealed five "normal" and five "reversed" polarity epochs of average duration 0.6–0.7 million years since the Middle Pliocene. Comparison of magnetic results by Cox, Doell, and Dalrymple (1963a, b) from radiometrically-dated late Cenozoic volcanic rocks from the western United States with data from Hawaii (McDougall and Tarling 1964), East Africa (Grommé and Hay 1963), and Europe indicates a rough correlation of polarity epochs going back about 3 m.y. and typically either ½ m.y. or 1 m.y. long, but with possible 25 per cent variations in length. A transition zone between reversely and normally polarized Mesozoic lavas in Basutoland (van Zijl, Graham, and Hales 1962) revealed an anticlockwise change of magnetic azimuths consistent with a westward drift of the geomagnetic field, and a drop in magnetic intensity supporting Elsasser's (1956) suggestion that the predominant dipole component of the field decreases to zero during such a reversal. The maximum time of this transition was estimated to be 12,000 years, similar to Hospers' and Janovsky's Cenozoic figures, whereas Elsasser's estimate based on the dynamo theory of the geomagnetic field is 3000–4000 years.

Without apparent bias, rocks with normal, reversed, and mixed polarization have all contributed to the large number of self-consistent palaeomagnetic results in the literature. The "time scale" that matters, therefore, is not the absolute length of a stable polarity epoch or of a transition period, as MacDonald implies, but the ratio of the latter to the former. This ratio, which in Hospers' and Janovsky's estimates is 1:100 to 4:100, also expresses the probability that a rock specimen subjected to palaeomagnetic measurement will have come from a transition zone. In view of the proliferation of palaeomagnetic work, this is not a seriously high probability for error, but more important, the very inconsistency of the data likely to be obtained from transitionally magnetized rocks will automatically disqualify them from use in palaeogeographic interpretation. Therefore, our present knowledge of reversed rock magnetization, much less than weakening confidence in palaeomagnetism, offers some of the most persuasive criteria in its support.

SUMMARY OF THE EVIDENCE

The palaeomagnetic information from Palaeozoic and younger rocks available at the end of 1964 is summarized in Figure 3. Regardless of rock polarity, all data have been plotted on a projection of the present Northern Hemisphere. The plots take three forms: (i) solid "polar wandering"

FIGURE 3. Polar movement since the Precambrian, relative to various land masses. Solid curves have been traced where the palaeomagnetic data from three or more levels in geological time follow a fairly consistent sequence. Otherwise broken lines have been used. The most detailed evidence is from Western Europe, the U.S.S.R., and North America, where solid portions of the curves in each case are based on over 40 separate palaeomagnetic determinations. Results from Britain, Tasmania, and Sakhalin are included with those from adjacent continents, but other off-shore islands are represented separately. Single pole positions are relative to: ■ China; ● Greenland; ▲ Madagascar. Letters refer to: (PЄ), Precambrian; Є, Cambrian; O, Ordovician; S, Silurian; D, Devonian; C, Carboniferous; P, Permian; TR, Triassic; J, Jurassic; K, Cretaceous; LT, MT, UT, Lower, Middle, and Upper Tertiary. Polar azimuthal projection of the present Northern Hemisphere.

curves, when a fairly large number of pole positions from three or more levels in time delineate a consistent path; (ii) dotted curves, when a vague pattern can be discerned but the detail is insufficient to establish a sequence confidently; (iii) single pole positions relevant only to single geological periods. Some curves consist of solid as well as dotted sections.

The individual data were taken either from original publications or from one of the catalogues by Irving (1960–62), Irving and Stott (1963), Cox and Doell (1960), and Kalashnikov (1961). Figure 3 incorporates a wide selection from this literature, no attempt having been made to exclude all but the most obviously unreliable data. As a result, the sample will include some dubious material, which may have to be revised or abandoned. Still, except for a few results where the catalogues had listed no error estimate, pole positions were incorporated into Figure 3 only if the associated confidence ovals had semiaxes of 20° arc length or less. In more than two-thirds of these data the length of the semiaxes was quoted to be in the range 5–15°. Neither the ovals nor individual pole positions used in plotting the curves are shown; details will be found in the original papers. On the basis of these figures, I estimate that the location of any point on solid portions of the curves may be trusted to about ten degrees; the dotted paths are much less certain.

Pole positions inferred from Tertiary igneous rocks in Figure 4 are distinguished according to (a) approximate age within the Tertiary, (b) land mass in which the rocks were sampled, and (c) magnetic polarity. There is no major conflict with Tertiary sedimentary data, which have been excluded only because the scatter in magnetization directions tended to be greater than in the igneous formations, particularly the fine-grained lavas. Reliable palaeomagnetic pole positions are also available from the Quaternary period, but have not been included because they are mostly distributed very close to the present spin pole. While this is an expected result, lending support to the axial dipole model, it cannot be applied to the continental drift problem.

Palaeomagnetic evidence from the Precambrian era has also been left out, though the literature includes much reliable material, especially from North America. Still, even the late Precambrian data, which account for the bulk of this evidence, must be regarded as inadequate for use in continental drift interpretations, perhaps with a single exception: the separation of late Precambrian pole positions relative to North America and Great Britain has been attributed to a widening of the gap between the two land masses by some 45° since that time (Du Bois 1958). For epochs earlier than a billion years, that is, the bulk of geological history, very few results from rock magnetism have yet been reported, and pertinent evidence from other fields is also scarce. For this immense time span, therefore, the information is inadequate even to sustain idle speculation on drift, a fact that implies the tremendous scope for new discoveries still awaiting palaeomagnetism.

Assessment of Reliability

No doubt much of the detail in Figure 3 will need revision. Confidence that the history depicted is, nevertheless, *broadly* factual can be justified by the large proportion of the incorporated data that satisfy one or more stability criteria. Furthermore, solid portions of the curves indicate that the

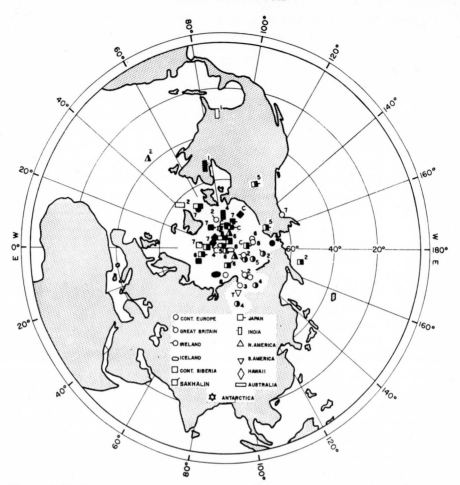

FIGURE 4. Tertiary pole positions from the palaeomagnetism of igneous rocks. Numbers refer to the age of the rocks as specified in the literature, in approximate time sequence as follows (hyphenation of two time units indicates either an overlap or uncertainty in age): 1, upper Cretaceous–lower Eocene; 2, Eocene, lower Tertiary, Palaeogene, Eocene-Oligocene; 3, Oligocene; 4, post-Eocene, Oligocene-Miocene; 5, Miocene; 6, Neogene, upper Tertiary, Miocene-Pliocene; 7, Pliocene; 8, Pliocene-Quaternary; T, Tertiary (undifferentiated); C, Cenozoic (undifferentiated). Symbols indicate land masses from which samples were obtained. Pole positions are shown by solid symbols when they have been calculated from rocks with "normal" polarity, i.e. magnetized in the present field sense; by hollow symbols when the rocks were of "reversed" polarity; and by half-solid symbols when a sequence of rocks of comparable age had "mixed," i.e. alternately "normal" and "reversed" polarity. Poles corresponding to rocks of "reversed" or "mixed" polarity have been transposed to the Northern Hemisphere. Polar azimuthal projection of the present Northern Hemisphere.

changes of pole positions with geological time are systematic. Admittedly, most of the detail is no finer than the average length of a geological period, say 60 m.y., corresponding to typical polar displacements of the order of 10°. With the fine structure smoothed in this way, however, the actual paths tend to be fairly direct, following a consistent time sequence at least within the portions shown solid. Hence the probability that the chronological trend of any *single* curve is accidental appears negligible.

Statistical analysis of the available evidence suggests that the striking divergence between *different* curves is also mostly significant. Irving (1964) compared the pole positions for a given geological period reported from palaeomagnetic studies in different parts of a single region, first with one another, then with contemporaneous poles from other regions. For the whole geological column between Precambrian and Pliocene, Irving found a strong tendency for the "within"-region poles to be in better agreement than those "between" regions.

Figure 3 is not greatly different from an earlier map (Deutsch 1963b) in which I had summarized the evidence available a few years ago. In the meantime, a large number of new results have appeared, most of them broadly conformable to the existing evidence but calling for some secondary changes on the map. An entirely new polar wandering path relative to the U.S.S.R. turns out to be close to the western European curve, as would be expected from the assumption that Europe and northern Asia have been a single, stable land mass since the Precambrian. It is too early to tell whether the two curves are significantly different.

Another new feature in Figure 3 is the first outline of a polar wandering curve for Newfoundland, which, predictably, is close to the North American curve. It incorporates some of the results of palaeomagnetic work in the Atlantic region of Canada (Table I), which are mostly of very recent origin and of special interest to this symposium. Black (1964), whose Palaeozoic poles relative to western Newfoundland (island) form the main basis of the curve, considers the discrepancy between these and contemporaneous poles relative to mainland North America to be significant and consistent with a 30° anticlockwise rotation of Newfoundland, perhaps largely during the Devonian. This example, therefore, illustrates the need to plot separate polar wandering curves for off-shore islands and the adjacent mainland, at least when either crustal unit is known to have been tectonically active.

A large number of results in Figure 4 are also backed by stability criteria. At first sight the pole positions seem to be distributed quite randomly about the present spin pole and, indeed, most authors still deduce from the Tertiary evidence that the Miocene and post-Miocene geomagnetic field, when averaged over periods of 10^3 years, was not significantly misaligned with the present spin axis. I think sufficient data already exist to justify modification of this view. Leaving aside the pre-Oligocene poles (nos. 1, 2), there emerges a non-random distribution with respect to longitude largely involving results from Eurasia, which the evidence from sedimentary rocks (not shown here) tends to supplement. While the co-latitude of these Eurasian poles is small (mostly 10–20°), their eccentric distribution with respect to the spin pole is probably significant, since in addition to other stability evidence the error ovals associated with about three-quarters of these poles exclude both the spin pole and geomagnetic pole. The polar wandering curves relative to Western Europe, the U.S.S.R., and Japan are

TABLE I

PALAEOMAGNETISM IN THE ATLANTIC PROVINCES AND GASPÉ

Three regions are distinguished: (1) Newfoundland, (2) Prince Edward Island, (3) the Mainland, which here includes New Brunswick and Gaspé. When more than one determination is available from contemporaneous rocks in the same region, an average pole position has been calculated, with equal weight given to each determination. The Precambrian average is from Irving (1964). Details may be found in the references.

Region	Rock formations	Age	No. of results averaged	Palaeomagnetic pole		References
				Lat.	Long.	
Newfoundland	Signal Hill and Blackhead sediments	Precambrian	2	11° N (11° S)	122° W (58° E)	Nairn et al. (1959)
Newfoundland	Bradore sediments	L. Cambrian	1	9° N	149° E	Black (1964)
Mainland	Ratcliffe Brook (N.B.) sediments	L. Cambrian	1	10° N	124° E	Black (1964)
Newfoundland	Clam Bank group sediments	L. Devonian	1	28° N	146° E	Black (1964)
Mainland	Perry (N.B.) volcanics and sediments	U. Devonian	2	31° N	115° E	Black (1964)
Newfoundland	Codroy group sediments	L. Carboniferous	2	36° N	133° E	Nairn et al. (1959) Black (1964)
Mainland	Bathurst (N.B.), Kennebecasis (N.B.), pre-Pictou (N.B.), Bonaventure (Gaspé) sediments	L. and U. Carboniferous	4	28° N	133° E	DuBois (1959) Black (1964)
Prince Edward Island	Red beds	Permo-Carboniferous	4	40° N	126° E	Roy (1963) Black (1964)

relevant to this Tertiary distribution. The Eurasian mainland data occupy the general region traversed by the first two curves, roughly between their Mesozoic to Lower Tertiary positions and the present pole. Such a trend would be expected if the polar or crustal movements reflected in these curves had persisted until relatively recent times.

Pending more detailed evidence, I attribute these results to small but significant amounts of continental drift during the Pliocene or later, and perhaps also between the Oligocene and Pliocene (Deutsch 1965). This interpretation would require reduction to 1 m.y. or so in the time interval over which rock magnetic data may be said to constitute evidence for the axial dipole assumption. The present commonly adopted value is about 20 m.y.

INTERPRETATION

If one accepts the palaeomagnetic evidence along with the axial dipole assumption, the earth's axis of rotation has been displaced through large angles relative to the crust since the Precambrian. Since continental drift is not the only mechanism capable of changing the co-ordinates of a point on the globe, the next step is to determine a cause. Two prominent alternatives to drift are *polar wandering* and *changes in the earth's circumference*. The former is defined as a shift of the earth's crust as a whole relative to the poles, the spin axis remaining "fixed" in space. In the absence of other criteria, polar wandering is as likely as continental drift to have produced any single curve in Figure 3.

If the earth changed in size, separate possibilities are *contraction* and *expansion*, both backed by major hypotheses (see e.g. Scheidegger 1958). While neither alternative has been abandoned, I shall consider only expansion, because it now seems to be somewhat better supported than contraction. Moreover, contraction, even if it had occurred, probably would have been too insubstantial to be measurable by palaeomagnetism. In any event, it turns out to be more difficult to distinguish in the record between continental drift and changes in the earth's circumference than to decide whether such hypothetical changes were positive or negative.

Any two or all three mechanisms (polar wandering, drift, expansion) could have occurred alternately or together. Since the same record has to serve all interpretations, it was convenient to tackle ambiguities by considering pairwise combinations.

Polar Wandering and Continental Drift

Hypothetical maps conforming to polar wandering, continental drift, or an alternation of the two are shown in Figure 5. While the polar wandering scheme is straightforward, producing the same curve relative to all crustal blocks, an infinity of displacements could have been chosen to illustrate drift. To some extent this scheme is qualitative, for neither the length of the curves nor their separation would necessarily reflect the true magnitude of

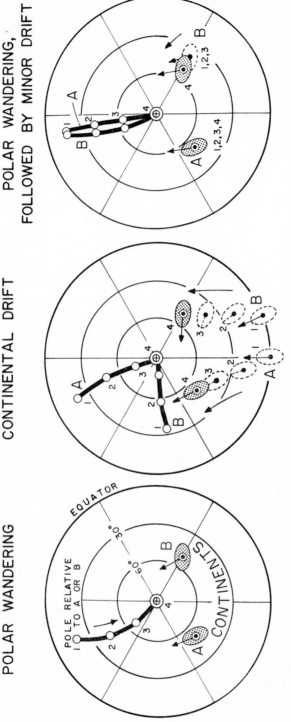

FIGURE 5. Schematic view of typical "polar wandering" curves inferred from palaeomagnetic data at two hypothetical continents, A and B. It is assumed that the rocks acquired a perfectly stable magnetization in the field of a geocentric dipole coaxial with the earth's spin axis. Numbers 1, 2, and 3 signify successive ancient positions of the poles and continents, and no. 4 marks their present positions. Polar paths are shown by solid lines. Arrows at A and B indicate original magnetization azimuths preserved in the rocks since time step 1; subsequent azimuths are not shown. Left: with no relative drift between continents, the same (arbitrarily chosen) polar path due to "pure" polar wandering is inferred at A and B. Centre: A and B have both drifted 50° northwards, increased their separation from 20° to 63° of arc, and rotated 60° and 30° anticlockwise, respectively. Right: separation of the curve inferred at B from the "pure" polar wandering curve relative to A has been caused by a 10° northward translation of B, without rotation.

drift—only "pure" translation along a meridian will do this. Extreme examples are: (i) the 90° rotation of a small, equatorial island about a palaeomagnetic sampling site, and (ii) translation of a large continent through 90° longitude along the Equator, without rotation. Case (i) would yield a "polar wandering" curve 90° long; case (ii) no curve at all. However, the actual drift motions would be likely to incorporate all possible components, i.e. translation along meridians and latitude circles as well as rotation, so that the distortions in the record due to single components tend to compensate one another. For this reason I have used composite motions to exemplify drift.

Most of the observed pattern in Figure 3 conforms closely to the continental drift scheme in Figure 5. In fact, the results cannot be interpreted in terms of polar wandering *without* drift. This might have disposed of the matter, were it not for the possibility that *both* mechanisms had operated, for as soon as the record indicates drift, the additional presence of polar wandering components becomes difficult to verify. Despite their possible association in the evidence, it is important to keep in mind the essential difference between these two hypothetical motions, which one would expect to proceed through basically different dynamics. This distinction is not always appreciated in the geological literature, but must be clearly recognized if one is to succeed in separating one motion from the other.

Velocity estimates in Table II (nos. 1–3) consider only the latitude component of drift, but probably the resultant displacements would proceed at rates of the same order. On the other hand, a theoretical model by Gold (1955) is consistent with motions two to four orders faster (Table III). The inherent concept in most serious treatments of polar wandering (Darwin 1877; Milankovitch 1934) is that it constitutes a movement of the *entire* earth, or at least mantle and crust, with respect to the axis, rather than *slippage* of the crust *over* the mantle. Gold attributed the damping of the observed short-period variations of latitude to dissipative deformation of the solid earth, essentially by plastic flow. Then a relatively modest redistribution of matter (perhaps due to some geological process) could instigate polar wandering through wide arcs in as little as 10^5–10^6 years. Unfortunately, such motions are easily missed in the record (Fig. 3), which probably still contains gaps amounting to some millions of years: even on Gold's more conservative estimate, this would be sufficient time for the pole to circle the earth. Continued enrichment of the record increases the chance that some rapid events will be detected, but so far there is no evidence for this.

Gold's paper appeared when the first path of polar migration, inferred from rock magnetism in Europe and North America, had just been published (Creer, Irving, and Runcorn 1954). This was not yet resolvable into separate curves, and hence open to more than one interpretation. However, most geophysicists were still reluctant to invoke large-scale drift, for it seemed implicit in Gold's argument that even if some part of the crust had, in fact, begun drifting, the resulting redistribution of mass would

TABLE II

MEAN VELOCITY OF HORIZONTAL DISPLACEMENTS WITH POSSIBLE RELEVANCE TO
CONTINENTAL DRIFT

The list represents a sample of typical estimates from the literature, and is not intended
to be exhaustive. The various minima and maxima therefore tend to express average rather
than extreme velocity estimates. For no. 10, the figures represent respectively an average
and a maximum velocity. In most other cases, the quoted range of estimates reflects
differences in the data from different land masses. Zero minima in nos. 1 and 4 indicate that
the displacement is not necessarily significant. Some details and references are given in the text.

No.	Type of estimate	Time span	Method	Mean velocity (cm/year)
1.	Latitude variation	Since Oligocene	Palaeomagnetic	0–3
2.	Latitude variation (India only)	Since Cretaceous	Palaeomagnetic	4–12
3.	Latitude variation (six land masses, India excluded)	Since Carboniferous	Palaeomagnetic	$\frac{1}{2}$–$2\frac{1}{2}$
4.	Latitude variation	20th century	Astronomical	0–6
5.	Relative fault motion	20th century	Geodetic and structural	4–5
6.	Relative fault motion	Since Mesozoic	Structural	$<\frac{1}{2}$–1
7.	Dispersal of Gondwanaland	Since Carboniferous	Palaeogeographic reconstruction	1–$3\frac{1}{2}$
8.	Latitude variation	Since Carboniferous	Palaeoclimatology (salt and corals)	$\frac{1}{2}$–$1\frac{1}{2}$
9.	Latitude variation	Since Cambrian	Palaeoclimatology (glaciation)	$1\frac{1}{2}$–$4\frac{1}{2}$
10.	Spreading of ocean floor	Since Cretaceous	Distance of islands from mid-ocean ridges	2–6
11.	Mantle convection	Unspecified	Thermal-hydrodynamic models	$\frac{1}{2}$–3

quickly initiate polar wandering of much larger proportions. This view might
have been vindicated if subsequent data from various continents had continued to fit the original curve (diagram at left in Figure 5), or conformed
to some pattern such as shown at right (but with the sequence reversed to
represent minor drift triggering large-scale polar wandering). Both models,
of course, were rendered untenable by the actual evidence.

On the basis of moment of inertia considerations, I have attempted to
show that continental drift, even of major proportions, need not provoke
more than modest, if any, polar wandering, (Deutsch 1963b). For pro-
longed stresses, moreover, the rheological condition of the mantle may be
that of a "Bingham" body of finite yield strength, with a relaxation time of
2×10^4 years or more (Scheidegger 1958). Polar wandering would then
be slowed down by three orders of magnitude compared with typical rates
derived from Gold's assumption. Maximum polar wandering velocities corresponding to my moment of inertia estimate and Scheidegger's model are
both in the range of a few centimetres per year, in agreement with typical
drift rates (Table III).

TABLE III

MEAN VELOCITY OF HORIZONTAL DISPLACEMENTS WITH POSSIBLE RELEVANCE TO EXPANSION OF THE EARTH OR POLAR WANDERING

The list represents a sample from the literature and is not intended to be exhaustive. Two estimates of latitude variation from Table II (nos. 1 and 4) have been used again, since they could be equally relevant to polar wandering and continental drift. Zero minima in these and three other cases indicate that the displacement is not necessarily significant. "Expansion" and "polar wandering" estimates included between the two broken lines are in the range covered by "continental drift" estimates in Table II. Some details are given in the text.

"Expansion of earth"			"Polar wandering"		
Type of estimate	Reference	Mean growth of earth's circumference (cm/year)	Type of estimate	Reference	Mean velocity (cm/year)
			Rheological model (time constant 10 years)	Gold (1955)	10^2–10^4
			Latitude variation, from astronomy	Lambert (1922); Munk and Macdonald (1960)	0–6
World-wide tectonics	Carey (1958)	2–4	Rheological model (time constant 2×10^4 years)	Scheidegger (1958)	0.5–5
			Latitude variation, from palaeomagnetism (since Oligocene)	Various authors	0–3
Growth of ocean basins; divergence of palaeo-magnetic polar wandering paths	Heezen (1959)	0.5–2	Mass redistribution due to drift	Deutsch (1963b)	0–2
Palaeomagnetism	Cox and Doell (1961)	0–0.6			
Decreased continental water cover; heat flow energy; growth of core	Egyed (1956)	0.2–0.5			
Energy sources in earth	Beck (1961); Cook and Eardley (1961)	0–0.3			
Growth of mid-ocean ridges	Wilson (1960)	0.06			
Decreased gravitational constant	Dicke (1962)	0.01–0.05			

This raises the question whether polar wandering could have *alternated* or *coincided* with continental drift, the two velocities now being of the same order. Irving (1958) suggests that drift was perhaps interrupted by quiet periods during which the poles wandered; if detected, such a sequence might enable one to reduce the alternatives for continental rearrangement to a small number. While no such alternations have been established, I think it is feasible that some "pure" polar wandering components may be still hidden in the record.

"Coincidence" between the two phenomena is a different and, strictly speaking, fallacious concept (Deutsch 1963*a*), since the phrase "crust as a whole" in the definition of polar wandering loses all meaning while the crust suffers disruption through drift. Coincidence becomes a less absurd notion if it is specified that polar wandering should relate only to portions of the globe *below* the crust, confining drift to the crust. Such artificial zoning, however, makes it impossible to *infer* polar wandering from continental data, regardless of the kind and volume of evidence used, if crustal blocks have drifted at the same time.

Continental Drift and Global Expansion

While the magnetic evidence clearly favours continental drift over polar wandering, an ambiguity remains between drift and possible expansion of the earth. Both models in Figure 6 could account for the large observed separations between the ancient and present poles (Fig. 3). Apparent polar wandering here results from the fact that after expansion the angle subtended at the earth's centre by two surface points a fixed distance apart will be smaller than before. The separation between the ancient and present pole positions is proportional to the ratio of the present to the ancient earth radii; the separation increases from zero for two palaeomagnetic sites located at the same ancient (and present) latitude, to a maximum when the sites lie along the same expanding meridian (Fig. 6).

The resulting decrease in the earth's curvature would set up stresses which, apart from local or irregular effects such as faulting, would cause the crust to be bent out of shape, thereby deflecting the remanent magnetization vectors in the rocks. However, even if a large land mass, such as Eurasia, were flattened against the surface of a globe expanding radially by a large amount, say 50 per cent, the maximum azimuth change of these vectors would not greatly exceed typical palaeomagnetic errors. For this reason, I shall neglect crustal bending as an aspect of expansion.

The same polar displacement would have been inferred in Figure 6 in the *absence* of contiguous territory between the sites, provided the distance between them had remained constant. Therefore, global expansion may also account for the separation of polar paths inferred at *different* land masses. However, the magnitude of this effect depends not only upon the amount of expansion, but also upon the nature of the resulting crustal rearrangements. Possible models are:

I. The continents maintained constant size and shape, and "polar wandering" curves result from their displacement not relative to each other, but relative to an imaginary co-ordinate system expanding with the geoid.

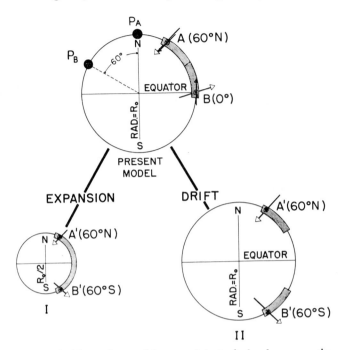

FIGURE 6. Alternative models to explain typical palaeomagnetic results. A meridional cross-section through the earth is shown. *A* and *B* are rock exposures of the same age on a hypothetical, continuous land mass, and *A'* and *B'* are locations *A* and *B* at the time the rocks were formed. Assuming a geocentric, axial dipole field, solid arrows are directed along the present field at *A* and *B*, and hollow arrows correspond to the ancient field direction preserved in the rocks. P_A and P_B are ancient North Pole positions inferred from the natural remanent magnetism of the rocks at *A* and *B*, respectively. Two alternative mechanisms, operating since the rocks were laid down, are consistent with the observations: (I) The earth has doubled its radius, and crustal blocks have remained constant in size; then, neglecting distortions due to the change in curvature, the latitude difference between the rock exposures was originally twice as large as at present. (II) The earth's radius has remained constant, but the rock sites were on separate land masses that subsequently drifted together. Palaeomagnetic observations at *A* and *B* cannot distinguish between models I and II.

II. Crustal blocks expanded on the same scale as the remaining earth, much in the manner of shapes painted upon the surface of an expanding balloon. If the field remained axially dipolar, this would produce no change in field direction at any palaeomagnetic site, and hence *no* polar paths. This example is purely schematic and has no basis in geological processes (not to be confused with "continental growth"), but emphasizes that global expansion would not necessarily bequeath a magnetic record to the rocks.

III. Crustal blocks maintained constant size and shape, each being regarded in crude fashion as the upper extension of a vertical column reaching into the mantle, to which the blocks are permanently attached. Expansion would then drive apart the land masses and supporting columns.

In a sense, model III constitutes the superposition of continental drift and expansion, though one could argue that this applies also to model I, for a mechanism in which the land masses all retain a frozen configuration ought to force some or all of them to drift over the expanding mantle. Paradoxically, model I constitutes classical drift in the physical sense but not according to the definition, whereas model III is drift according to the definition but not in any physical sense.

Obviously, large stresses must be relieved in model III as well: this would cause long, vertical fissures, widening as the earth continued to grow. Not surprisingly, oceanographers who favour expansion, but wish to achieve this without forcing sialic blocks through the sima or invoking convection currents, favour model III. Thus, Heezen (1960) proposed such a model after studying the mid-oceanic ridge system with its characteristic median rift. He postulates that expansion of the earth's exterior caused the widening under tension of palaeo-rifts of this kind, which have grown into the existing ocean basins. With no change in continental area, this would imply almost doubling the earth's radius within geological history.

Heezen similarly seeks to account for the divergence of the palaeo-magnetic pole tracks (such as Fig. 3), but there is an infinity of possible interpretations. For example, the rock magnetism at sampling sites located on different land masses would record no change if these neither rotated with respect to the meridian nor changed latitude as they separated during expansion. Though this is a special and perhaps unlikely case of model III, the actual surface pattern caused by global expansion plausibly would be a resultant of unrecorded motions of the latter type and partly or fully recorded phenomena as in model I or Figure 6.

Carey (1958) invokes rates of expansion even larger than Heezen's, and increasing with time. He maintains that expansion of the earth during geological history is not only compatible with large-scale crustal shifts, which he infers from oroclines and other tectonic considerations, but quite essential in interpreting details of drift. Before seeking clues in the magnetic evidence, one would like to know whether such vast expansions are physically plausible. Thus, if Heezen's proposal is to explain Figure 3, the radial increase since the early Palaeozoic cannot have been much less than 50 per cent. When this is compared with the estimate from his oceanographic model, Heezen's mechanism would inflate the earth by a volume factor of 3 to 8 during part or all of geological history, and is therefore apt to raise new and serious problems, especially of an astronomical nature.

Mean expansion rates estimated by other authors are given in Table III. All except Carey's and Heezen's figures are one to two orders of magnitude smaller than those typical of continental drift. It follows that *minor to moderate* expansion, if it occurred, would be difficult to infer from maps such as Figure 3.

In a test proposed by Egyed (1960), two sampling sites lying along the same palaeomagnetic meridian in *continuous* territory, as in Figure 6, are considered. From the respective magnetic dips at the two sites one infers palaeolatitudes and compares their difference d_a with the angular separation d_p of the palaeolatitude circles measured along the present earth's surface; the ratio d_a/d_p equals the ratio r_p/r_a of present to ancient earth radii. Later Egyed (1961) modified this procedure so that results from sites not on the same palaeomagnetic meridian could be used. In either case, the land mass should be as large as possible, suggesting Eurasia as the best choice.

Cox and Doell (1961) applied this test to published palaeomagnetic results from Permian rock formations in western Europe and northern Siberia. The Permian period is well chosen, for rock magnetism reveals a notable absence of major fluctuations in the earth's field during that time. Cox and Doell conclude that their test neither confirms nor rejects moderate expansions, such as Egyed's, but is inconsistent with more drastic growth since the Permian. Results of a similar study by Ward (1963), based on Devonian and younger rocks also in Europe and Siberia, support Cox and Doell's estimate, but van Hilten (1963), from his own application of the test, concludes that expansion since the Carboniferous is "not improbable," even on the large scale proposed by Carey.

I think none of these estimates can be regarded as final until much more magnetic evidence is available, permitting refinement of the test and its extension to other land masses. In the meantime, I have listed in Table III only the more conservative estimate by Cox and Doell.

Global Expansion and Polar Wandering

As long as expansion and polar wandering remain separate alternatives, axial shifts within an expanding earth are also possible. Separation of these motions in polar wandering maps would be difficult, because crustal changes brought about by expansion may be geometrically indistinguishable from drift and hence introduce into the evidence the inherent ambiguity already noted in the case of drift vs. polar wandering. However, if one accepts that large-scale expansion and polar wandering, while possible, were both unlikely events, their superposition becomes even less likely.

Reality and Time-table of Drift

In summary, rock magnetism supports the occurrence of continental drift since the Precambrian. Resolution is not better than about the length of a geological period. Alternation of drift with polar wandering up to four orders of magnitude faster than this cannot yet be ruled out, but no evidence for such motions has been found. "Simultaneous" polar wandering and drift is an ambiguous concept and, in any case, cannot be diagnosed from measurements in the earth's crust. Global expansion could also account for the magnetic results from different land masses, provided the radial increase since the early Palaeozoic was large, say not less than 50 per cent. Palaeomagnetic tests in a single, large continent can distinguish such grandiose expansions from drift, but initial applications of the test, as well as theoretical objections, seem to rule against their occurrence. Radial growth one or two orders slower than estimated drift rates is more feasible, but could not alone account for the observed separations of polar wandering curves. In the absence of still other explanations, continental drift remains the only essential component in the palaeomagnetic maps.

However, the occurrence of drift is much easier to deduce than any detailed history. While Table II suggests typical mean drift velocities of a few centimeters per year, one must ask whether the mechanism itself is "typical," i.e. characterized by continuous or repeated displacements of crustal blocks during much of geological history. Many authors answer in the negative, e.g. Runcorn (1962), who maintains that drift took place during a "surprisingly recent time" compared with the earth's age. While this would conform to his postulate that drift was initiated only after the pattern of convection currents in the mantle changed to a harmonic of degree 5—a unique event occurring in the last 200 m.y.—there is no evidence that drift was, indeed, confined to such a unique time span. From detailed analyses of palaeomagnetic maps, Creer (1964) infers the presence of drift components since the Permian or late Carboniferous. The rotation of Newfoundland deduced by Black (1964) would advance the time-table for (modest) drift to the Devonian. Present interpretations probably cannot go further; until better maps are available, the possibility of drift during the early Palaeozoic and Precambrian must be left open.

Rock Magnetism in the Appalachian Region

Easternmost Canada offers a fertile field for palaeomagnetism, with potential applications that bear directly upon continental drift. The problems concerned are largely *tectonic* or *structural*. With some exceptions (e.g. Norris and Black 1961), the published work on this aspect of rock magnetism is still sparse in comparison with the copious literature dealing with palaeomagnetism relative to large land masses. Since tectonic and structural matching must be chronologically as well as geometrically precise, such studies call for a close integration between rock magnetism and radiometric or other methods of determining age. The following is a brief, by no means exhaustive, list of potential problems in the Atlantic region, which are mostly interrelated. I have assumed in each case that rocks suitable for palaeomagnetism will be found, though of course this is uncertain.

1. *Correlation of structures across the North Atlantic.* Wilson (1962) applies the name "Cabot fault" to a narrow belt of large faults extending from New England to Nova Scotia and Newfoundland, probably crossing

the Bay of Fundy and Cabot Strait. He suggests that the "Cabot" and Great Glen faults of Scotland, which are probably of comparable (Devonian to Upper Carboniferous) age, may be the two ends of a single transcurrent fault. Most continental drift reconstructions (e.g. Du Toit 1937) place Palaeozoic Newfoundland in the vicinity of the British Isles. If so, one would expect to find evidence in truncated fold belts, as well as interrupted faults. A possible example of a match is the Lower Palaeozoic structures in north-eastern Newfoundland and western Ireland. Rock magnetism would support such correlations if the magnetic dips of pertinent rock formations on opposite Atlantic coasts turned out to be similar, and their magnetic azimuths could be aligned by alignment of the structures along postulated trends.

2. *Rotation of Newfoundland*. Existing evidence for the 30° anticlockwise rotation of western Newfoundland with respect to the mainland (Black 1964) rests largely upon magnetic comparisons between Palaeozoic rock formations in Newfoundland and those in New Brunswick, Prince Edward Island, and Gaspé (Table I). Less convincingly, Nairn *et al.* (1959) infer a 20° post-Carboniferous anticlockwise rotation of Newfoundland based on Precambrian and Carboniferous rock magnetism on that island and in the United States. To strengthen the evidence these studies should be extended and include, if possible, a palaeomagnetic comparison between the island of Newfoundland and the coast of Labrador.

3. *Unbending of oroclines*. According to Carey (1955), an *orocline* is the impressed strain in an originally linear orogenic system "flexed in plan to a horse-shoe or elbow shape" by stresses postdating its main period of genesis. Based on this concept, some of the larger "oroclines" (e.g. in Alaska) become hinges about which continental blocks may have rotated (Wilson 1958). Some reconstructions inferred by Carey purely from orocline tectonics agree strikingly with rotations deduced from subsequent palaeomagnetic results (e.g. the supposed Cenozoic bending of Japan; Kawai *et al.* 1961). I think the Appalachian region of Canada lends itself well to a palaeomagnetic test of the orocline hypothesis. At first sight, for example, there appears to be a bend in the structure between Cape Breton Island and mainland Nova Scotia, which may prove to be a true orocline, with its pivot in the vicinity of Camso Strait. While this is pure speculation, it may be well worth making a test by comparing the magnetization of Carboniferous and Lower Palaeozoic (or Precambrian) rocks on Cape Breton Island with those in the mainland maritime provinces .

4. *Palaeomagnetism of the Grand Banks of Newfoundland*. The existence of numerous high shoals to the east and southeast of the Avalon Peninsula opens an entirely new prospect to palaeomagnetism. An aqualung descent to the Virgin Rocks, 130 miles southeast of St. John's pioneered by Memorial University in 1964 (Lilly 1965) showed that the shoals are accessible to direct geological study; this means that divers could collect oriented samples for rock magnetism. A second cruise to the Virgin Rocks (Lilly and Deutsch

1966) led to the successful recovery of a number of samples of shoal rock, which had been oriented *in situ* by divers. Two of the high shoal areas, Tail of the Banks and Flemish Cap, are respectively 300 and 400 miles from land, allowing palaeomagnetic observations to extend as far as one-fifth of the distance to Europe. Obviously, the usefulness of such studies will be limited unless they are related to existing or future information from other kinds of geophysical and geological investigation in the northwest Atlantic.

5. *Polar wandering curves.* The above applications are mainly regional in character, but there is also scope for the more traditional service of rock magnetism, that of outlining a history of the geomagnetic field. The largest gaps in this record usually correspond to rocks of Precambrian and Lower Palaeozoic times. The Appalachian region, however, is well endowed with Proterozoic, Cambrian, Ordovician, and Silurian formations, apart from younger Palaeozoic rocks. While the rocks in this region are often badly deformed or metamorphosed, enough raw material suitable for rock magnetism studies is likely to remain to augment or modify those sections of the polar wandering curves relative to North America that are now most weakly supported.

References

BECK, A. E. (1961). Energy requirements of an expanding earth. J. Geophys. Res., *66*: 1485–1490.

BLACK, R. F. (1964). Palaeomagnetic support of the theory of rotation of the western part of the island of Newfoundland. Nature, *202*: 945–948.

BLACKETT, P. M. S., CLEGG, J. A., and STUBBS, P. H. S. (1960). An analysis of rock magnetic data. Proc. Roy. Soc. (London), Ser. A, *256*: 291–322.

BRUNHES, B. (1906). Recherches sur la direction d'aimantation des roches volcaniques. J. de Phys., *5*: 705–724.

BULLARD, E. C. (1949). The magnetic field within the earth. Proc. Roy. Soc. (London), Ser. A, *147*: 433.

CAREY, S. W. (1955). The orocline concept in geotectonics—Part I. Papers and Proc., Roy. Soc. Tasmania, *89*: 255–288.

———— (1958). The tectonic approach to continental drift. *In* Continental Drift, a Symposium, pp. 177–355. Hobart, Tasmania: Geology Dept., Univ. of Tasmania.

CHEVALLIER, R. (1925). L'aimantation des laves de l'Etna et l'orientation du champ terrestre en Sicile du XIIe au XVIIe siècle. Ann. de Phys., *4*: 5–162.

COOK, M. A. and EARDLEY, A. J. (1961). Energy requirements in terrestrial expansion. J. Geophys. Res., *66*: 3907–3912.

COX, A. and DOELL, R. R. (1960). Review of paleomagnetism. Bull. Geol. Soc. Amer., *71*: 645–768.

———— (1961). Palaeomagnetic evidence relevant to a change in the earth's radius. Nature, *189*: 45–47.

COX, A., DOELL, R. R., and DALRYMPLE, G. B. (1963a). Geomagnetic polarity epochs and Pleistocene geochronometry. Nature, *198*: 1049–1051.

———— (1963b). Geomagnetic polarity epochs: Sierra Nevada II. Science, *142*: 382–385.

CREER, K. M. (1964). A reconstruction of the continents for the Upper Palaeozoic from palaeomagnetic data. Nature, *203*: 1115–1120.

CREER, K. M., IRVING, E., and RUNCORN, S. K. (1954). The direction of the geomagnetic field in remote epochs in Great Britain. J. Geomag. Geoelec., *6*: 163–168.

DARWIN, G. H. (1877). On the influence of geological changes on the earth's axis of rotation. Phil. Trans. Roy. Soc., *167*: 271.

DEUTSCH, E. R. (1963a). Polar wandering—A phantom event? Amer. J. Sci., *261*: 194–199.

———— (1963b). Polar wandering and continental drift: An evaluation of recent evidence. *In* Polar Wandering and Continental Drift, *edited by* A. C. Munyan, pp. 4–46. Tulsa: Society of Economic Paleontologists and Mineralogists, Spec. Publ. 10.

———— (1965). The paleolatitude of Tertiary oil fields. J. Geophys. Res., *70*: 5193–5203.

DICKE, R. H. (1962). The earth and cosmology. Science, *138*: 653–664.

DU BOIS, P. M. (1958). Palaeomagnetism and geological correlation. Ann. de Géophys., *14*: 509–514.

———— (1959). Palaeomagnetism and rotation of Newfoundland. Nature, *184*: 63–64.

DU TOIT, A. L. (1937). Our Wandering Continents. New York: Hafner.

EGYED, L. (1956). A new theory on the internal constitution of the earth and its geological-geophysical consequences. Acta Geol. Acad. Sci. Hung., *4*: 43–83.

———— (1960). Some remarks on continental drift. Geofis. pura e appl., *45*: 115–116.

———— (1961). Palaeomagnetism and the ancient radii of the earth. Nature, *190*: pp. 1097–1098.

ELSASSER, W. M. (1956). Hydromagnetic dynamo theory. Rev. Mod. Phys., *28*: 135–163.

EVERITT, C. W. F. (1962). Self-reversal of magnetization in a shale containing pyrrhotite. Phil. Mag., *7*: 831–842.

FISHER, R. (1953). Dispersion on a sphere. Proc. Roy. Soc. (London), Ser. A, *217*: 295–305.

GILBERT, W. (1600). De Magnete. London: Peter Short. [Engl. transl. by P. F. MOTTELY (1958). New York: Dover.]

GOLD, T. (1955). Instability of the earth's axis of rotation. Nature, *175*: 526–534.

GRAHAM, J. W. (1949). The stability and significance of magnetism in sedimentary rocks. J. Geophys. Res., *54*: 131–167.

GROMMÉ, C. S. and HAY, R. L. (1963). Magnetization of bed I, Olduvai Gorge, Tanganyika. Nature, *200*: 560–561.

HEEZEN, B. C. (1959). Paleomagnetism, Continental Displacements and the Origin of Submarine Topography. Intern. Oceanog. Congr. Preprints, 26. Washington: Amer. Assoc. Adv. Sci.

———— (1960). The rift in the ocean floor. Sci. Amer., *203*: 98–110.

HILTEN, D. VAN (1963). Palaeomagnetic indications of an increase in the earth's radius. Nature, *200*: 1277–1279.

HOLMES, A. (1965). Principles of Physical Geology, rev. ed. London: Thomas Nelson.

HOSPERS, J. (1955). Rock magnetism and polar wandering. J. Geol., *63*: 59–73.

HUMBOLDT, A. VON (1797). Über die merkwürdige magnetische Polarität einer Gebirgskuppe von Serpentinstein. Greus Neues J. Physik, *4*: 136–140.

IRVING, E. (1958). Palaeogeographic reconstruction from palaeomagnetism. Geophys. J., *1*: 224–237.

———— (1960–62). Palaeomagnetic pole positions, part I. Geophys. J., *3*: 96–111. Palaeomagnetic directions and pole positions, parts II–V. Geophys. J., *3*: 444–449; *5*: 70–79; *6*: 263–267; *7*: 263–274.

———— (1964). Paleomagnetism and Its Application to Geological and Geophysical Problems. New York: John Wiley.

IRVING, E. and STOTT, P. M. (1963). Palaeomagnetic directions and pole positions, part VI. Geophys. J., *8*: 249–257.

JANOVSKY, B. M. (1962). Probleme des Paläomagnetismus in der UdSSR. Deut. Akad. Wiss. Berlin, Geomag. Inst. Potsdam, Publ. no. 29, pp. 37–59.

JOHNSON, E. A., MURPHY, T., and TORRESON, O. W. (1948). Pre-history of the earth's magnetic field. Terr. Mag., *53*: 349–372.

KALASHNIKOV, A. C. (1961). The history of the geomagnetic field. Bull. Acad. Sci. USSR, Geophys. Ser., pp. 1243–1279. [Engl. Transl. Amer. Geophys. Union (1962), pp. 819–838.]

KAWAI, N., ITO, H., and KUME, S. (1961). Deformation of the Japanese islands inferred from rock magnetism. Geophys. J., *6*: 124–130.

KHRAMOV, A. N. (1958). Palaeomagnetic Correlation of Sedimentary Rocks. Leningrad: Gostoptekhizdat.

Lambert, W. (1922). The interpretation of apparent changes in mean latitude. Astron. J., *34*: 103–110.

Lilly, H. D. (1965). Submarine examination of the Virgin Rocks area, Grand Banks, Newfoundland: Preliminary note. Bull. Geol. Soc. Amer., *76*: 131–132.

Lilly, H. D. and Deutsch, E. R. (1966). Recovery of oriented samples for palaeomagnetism by aqualung divers, Grand Banks of Newfoundland. To be published.

MacDonald, G. J. F. (1963). The deep structure of continents. Rev. Geophys., *1*: 587–665.

McDougall, I. and Tarling, D. H. (1964). Dating geomagnetic polarity zones. Nature, *202*: 171–172.

Milankovitch, M. (1934). Der Mechanismus der Polverlagerungen und die daraus sich ergebenden Polbahnkurven. Gerlands Beitr. zur Geophys., *42*: 70–97.

Munk, W. H. and MacDonald, G. J. F. (1960). The Rotation of the Earth. London: Cambridge Univ. Press.

Nagata, T., Akimoto, S., and Uyeda, S. (1952–53). Self-reversal of thermoremanent magnetism of igneous rocks (I, II, and III). J. Geomag. Geoelec., *4*: 22–38, 102–107; *5*: 168–184.

Nairn, A. E. M., Frost, D. V., and Light, B. G. (1959). Palaeomagnetism of certain rocks from Newfoundland. Nature, *183*: 596–597.

Néel, L. (1948). Propriétés magnétiques des ferrites; ferrimagnétisme et anti-ferromagnétisme. Ann. de Phys., *3*: 137–198.

Norris, D. K. and Black, R. F. (1961). Application of palaeomagnetism to thrust mechanics. Nature, *192*: 933–935.

Roy, J. L. (1963). Palaeomagnetism of Prince Edward Island. Geophys. J., *8*: 226–230.

Runcorn, S. K. (1954). The earth's core. Trans. Amer. Geoph. Union, *35*: 49–63.

——— (1959). On the hypothesis that the mean geomagnetic field for parts of geological time has been that of a geocentric axial multipole. J. Atmos. Terrest. Phys., *14*: 167–174.

——— (1962). Convection currents in the earth's mantle. Nature, *195*: 1248–1249.

Scheidegger, A. E. (1958). Principles of Geodynamics. Berlin: Springer Verlag.

Ward, M. A. (1963). On detecting changes in the earth's radius. Geophys. J. *8*: 217–225.

Wilson, D. W. R. (1958). The orocline concept and continental drift—A commentary. Symposium: Polar Wandering and Continental Drift. J. Alta. Soc. Petrol. Geol., *6*: 174–178.

Wilson, J. T. (1960). Some consequences of expansion of the earth. Nature, *185*: 880–882.

——— (1962). Cabot fault, an Appalachian equivalent of the San Andreas and Great Glen faults and some implications for continental displacement. Nature, *195*: 135–138.

Wilson, R. L. and Everitt, C. W. F. (1963). Thermal demagnetization of some Carboniferous lavas for palaeomagnetic purposes. Geophys. J., *8*: 149–164.

Zijl, J. S. V. van, Graham, K. W. T., and Hales, A. L. (1962). The palaeomagnetism of the Stormberg lavas of South Africa (I and II). Geophys. J., *7*: 23–39, 169–182.

THE ANCIENT FLORA AND
CONTINENTAL DRIFT

N. W. Radforth, F.R.S.C.

CHALONER (1959), one of our most active British palaeobotanists, attempted the analysis and assessment of recent geophysical evidence in relation to the plant world. Despite the fact that the mechanics of drift as conceived by Wegener involved the application of forces of irrational size, Chaloner was impressed by the accumulation of palaeomagnetic evidence, for both polar wandering and continental drift. Heretofore palaeobotanists have had to assume that the poles must have moved from time to time and that the great areas supporting plant life must have moved with respect to one another. Sahni (1936) 30 years ago attempted to justify this assumption. Chaloner (1959) encourages the view that it is time to ascribe a realistic value to these dynamic features of the earth and states: "Now if the contribution of palaeomagnetism to the controversy cannot be said to have 'proved' the occurrence of drift, it can fairly be claimed to have made it a more respectable hypothesis." He reaches this decision through several considerations, one of these being that: "The palaeomagnetic data are therefore consistent with India and Australia having moved from positions relatively close to the Antarctic continent, into their present locations, during Tertiary Times." He shows that these new positions involve "exactly the same direction and order of drift postulated by Du Toit on the basis of geological data unconnected with palaeomagnetism." This conclusion is comforting to palaeobotanists, for the Du Toit concepts were basic in accounting for distributional phenomena among the ancient flora.

It remains to be stated that, among the palaeobotanical proponents of the drift theory, there is a realization that thought must be given to the question of the time at which drifting took place. The significant time for break-up of the southern land complex is claimed by the geologists as being no later than the Tertiary, as much as 100 million years after the great mid-atlantic rift commenced with the New Siberian Islands as its fulcrum.

According to the interpretation of Stubbs (1964) the continents of the Southern Hemisphere drifted apart earlier than in the Tertiary, the process in his view having started sometime in the Mesozoic. From palaeobotanical evidence, however, it must be claimed that some signs of secondary continental differentials in composition occur in flora older than Mesozoic. Mrs. Plumstead's discovery of *Scutum* in the Transvaal is a case in point (Plumstead 1958). Whether the claim can be made that *Scutum* represents the primitive angiosperm character or not, the genus with its five species signifies *divergence* within the Glossopteris and the contrast with *Angara* constituents of the Northern Hemisphere that convey divergence, for example Vojnov-skyales (Andrews 1961, p. 351), is marked, though seed production is involved in both.

At present, the palaeobotanist sees more plausibility in the drift theory than he once did because of three major assertions of the theory:

1. Past climatic zones have moved by influences other than ice advance.

2. Climatic zones have been "warped" or distorted *possibly* by differential rates of movement of land masses.

3. Major continental disintegration and separation appears to have begun in the Tertiary in what is now the Southern Hemisphere and in the Mesozoic in the Northern Hemisphere.

One might ask whether there is any other plausible geological or related contribution that the palaeobotanist can use. Kolbe (1957), in his claim that a lake bed existed in a now submerged Atlantic island, draws our attention to the possible existence of land bridges. The one to which Kolbe's evidence would refer is the mid-Atlantic ridge. That this was in fact a bridge facilitating migration of plant life is not without evidence, for Kolbe has produced evidence of diatoms and epidermal tissue of grasses and sedges from his proposed lake bed. (The site of this discovery is 1000 km west of Africa at 10° N latitude.) It must be remembered, however, that the growth of this type of plant life could have been started by migrating birds, for example, the black-browed albatross. Undoubtedly, there were "aerial" bridges in the past as there are today. The possibility that relative crustal motions are concentrated in narrow rift zones may provide an attractive opportunity to apply palaeobotanical tests on a small scale. For instance, the flora (probably Mesozoic) in northeastern Ellesmere Island, exposed recently by the author and his colleagues, may or may not have counterparts in northeastern Greenland. Differences may be observable, between these flora, because of separation by the Baffin Bay rift (Fig. 1), and the consequent westward displacement of the Ellesmere types, but there should be no displacement between the flora of Ellesmere and of other islands of the Canadian Arctic, because they are on the same side of the rift.

A few years ago Chaloner (1959) made no reference to the significance of active ridges as applied to palaeobotanical problems. The palaeomagnetic research, on the other hand, led him to state (p. 29): "it [palaeomagnetic research] has helped to create an atmosphere in which the biological evidence may be examined anew on its own merits." By reason of the ridge-rift theory the observation may be endorsed with even greater enthusiasm.

THE NATURE OF THE FOSSIL PLANT

Plants of the past are seldom found as whole organisms. In contrast to animal fossils, those of plants are usually preserved as fragments and they are named as such. For instance ferns are recorded in the rocks as rhizomes,

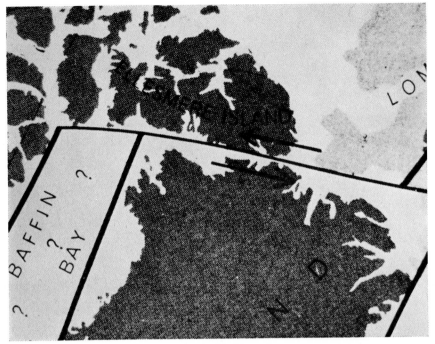

FIGURE 1

fronds, fructifications, or spores, and knowledge of the plant *in toto* is gained only through laborious palaeobotanical analyses, which result in reconstructions if the investigator is fortunate enough to achieve this end.

Palaeobotanists have grown used to making age designations or morphological analyses based on mere segments of fronds or on fructifications (Fig. 2). More often than not spores or pollen (microfossils) are as distinctive and peculiar to species as is the plant as a whole. In assessing a flora, conclusions are usually reached by consideration of assemblages of fragments, which may have to be identified by examination of their cuticular surfaces.

The mechanics of fossilization creates several kinds of fossils. There are compressions (flattened carbonaceous remains) and petrifactions in which tissues are preserved three-dimensionally by infiltration and partial or whole mineralization. These two types are the commonest and offer the possibility of disclosing diagnostic features. In some fossil locations there is a recurrence of assemblages of botanical character. These are used in establishing morphological and sometimes physiological values and they occasionally have stratigraphic or age significance. They are used to delineate the presence of environmental and evolutionary trends if the number of entities is sufficiently great.

It often happens that because plant microfossils are only fragments of whole plants, it is not possible to designate conclusively their true natural affinity as to species, genus, or sometimes larger taxa. Thus, a common situation is that a well-known fossil, for example, the compression *Archaeop-*

FIGURE 2. Fertile segments of a frond of Archaeopterus; a compression from the upper
Devonian of Ellesmere Island.

teris sp., has an uncertain taxonomic connection. It may be fern-like (as is
indeed the case for *Archaeopteris*), but there is always the possibility that
seeds may be found in organic connection with the fronds to make it a seed
plant. Also, the morphological resemblance that one species of, say, *Archaeopteris* has to another may be as artificial as that between a pine leaf and
certain grass leaves if one encountered incomplete fossilized remains of
them. Among microfossils this situation sometimes occurs: for example,
oak pollen grains resemble those of African violets.

Despite the impossibility of applying a test of confidence to many microfossils, use is made of artificial genera for stratigraphic and climatic indices.
Archaeopteris, for example, was for many years taken unquestioningly as
signifying Upper Devonian, although now it is known to occur sparingly in
Middle Devonian as well.

There is some safety in predicting that microfossils will become the organic
reference material of major importance in considerations of the drift hypothesis. The last five to ten years have revealed that vast numbers of distinctive
spores appear in sedimentary rocks, and these assemblages have already
proved their worth in petroleum exploration. In a deep section of outcrop
in the Gaspé Devonian, where only about a dozen plant macrofossils are
known, an assemblage of several dozen distinctive microfossils has been
turned out of a segment of the section measuring only approximately 2 cm
in thickness (Radforth and Wilkinson 1959). There is as much, if not more,
potential geological evidence in a single microspore 50 μ in diameter as
there is in many a fragmentary macroscopic plant compression.

To date, the palaeobotanical problem of determining the undoubted relationship between plant material on widely disjoint land masses has rested on recognition of certain so-called floras (as distinct from species, genera, or single taxa of any size). Also, when attempting to account for the ability of warm-climate plants of the past to grow in what are now the frigid polar zones, floras are the bases on which judgment rests.

To assess this situation, it might be helpful to designate the floras involved in the drift question, and this is the purpose of the following section.

THE FOUR GREAT FLORAS AND THE CASE FOR DRIFT

The students of both the drift and permanence hypotheses invariably allude to the Glossopteris flora shared by India, South and Central Africa, southern South America, Australia, and Antarctica. The magnitude of spread between related components of this flora is impressive. The separation involves the Indian Ocean, the South Pacific, and the South Atlantic.

Krishnan (1954) identifies the flora with its base in Upper Carboniferous and its culmination in mid-Cretaceous. Two genera, *Glossopteris* and *Gangamopteris*, totalling 58 species, are best known from leaf studies. The leaves may be 3 cm in length but occur up to 40 cm and are spatulate, ovate, or linear in shape. They are now known to belong to seed plants but originally were thought to be foliage of ferns. Conifer wood is included in the flora, and articulated plants apparently flourished (Krishnan 1954). It is only recently that the lycopodophytes have been regarded as occurring significantly. Their fossil record is derived almost entirely from microfossil studies. Andrews (1961) points out that the recent study on the *Glossopteris*-type foliage emphasizes artificiality of relationship. The difference in seed and seed-like structures associated with the organs is the basis for this view, and his idea seems to be well founded. The climate of all habitats was apparently influenced by the wide glaciation of Gondwanaland, and it is claimed that a cool temperate condition existed.

Another more prolific and divergent flora occurred in the Northern Hemisphere, the Euroamerican flora. It was geographically controlled in southern Europe by the Variscan-Armorican Mountains stretching from Germany into Ireland via France. In what is now North America, the Appalachian Uplift and the seashore to the east provided one zone. In the heart of the continent, deposits were limited to the west by the ancient Rocky Mountains. Seed plants occurred for certain, the conifers came into existence as did the mosses, the club mosses, the horsetails, and tree ferns. From studies of macrofossils alone, it would appear that the great majority of modern "forms" of plant life, if not taxa, came into being. In addition six great groups rose, flourished, and fell: the Lepidodendrales, the Calamites, the Sphenophyllales, the Coenopteridales, the Seed Ferns, and the Cordaites. Overlap into time zones above and below, when it occurred, was slight.

The classicists claim a warm, humid, subtropical climate for the Euramerican flora. Arnold (1947) lays emphasis on the comparison of the organic deposits of middle and late Palaeozoic with those of modern times in alluding to climate. The claim is that present-day peat forms primarily in temperate conditions, not as did the peat of the past in subtropical swelter with only slight seasonal fluctuation.

A third so-called flora—the Angara—was contained by the Urals, the Arctic Ocean, and the Pacific Ocean. It merged in outer Mongolia with the fourth, the Cathaysia flora, reaching from what is now Korea to the southern extremity of southeast Asia (Fig. 3).

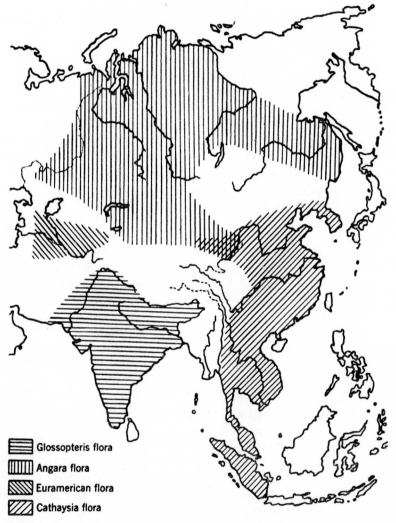

Glossopteris flora

Angara flora

Euramerican flora

Cathaysia flora

FIGURE 3. Late Palaeozoic–early Mesozoic floras. From Andrews (1961), after Halle (1937).

In the Angara flora, corditean-like leaves are called *Noeggeratheopsis*. These, 17 species of them, occur with ferns, sphagnalean-like mosses, and the distinctive *Vojnovskya*, a gymnosperm (Fig. 4), which is unique in the Angara flora. Traditionally the claim stands that the assemblage enjoyed a temperate climate.

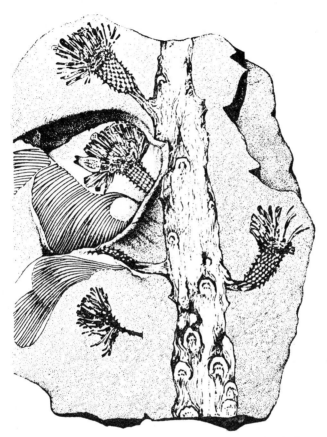

FIGURE 4. *Vojnovskya paradoxa*, gymnosperm. From Andrews (1961), after Neuberg (1955).

Gegantopteris and *Taeniopteris* supply the theme of characterization for the Cathaysia flora. One species of the latter had leaves which in Andrews' words (1961): "Very likely . . . appeared similar to a fair sized banana leaf in life." Any evidence that the climate of the Cathaysia flora was warm in contrast to moderate is lacking. Opinion sides with moderate.

The list of features in Table I summarizes the points of argument thought to be critical in relating all the floras to the idea of drift.

The application of the information in Table I affords a basis for argument, not necessarily for conclusion. Obviously, if arguments favouring one trend of logic or another could be supplied from a fresh approach, they

TABLE I

The Four Great Floras Relative to Drift vs. Permanence

1. They are distinctive structurally, i.e. despite artificiality in nomenclature.
2. Each shows some specificity within its own complex of major taxa.
3. Each has special geomorphic delineation at its geographic limits.
4. None is a true "flora" in that each pertains for a series of major time zones, etc.
5. Consensus of classical opinion arranges them as to general climate as follows: Glossopteris—cold; Angara—moderate; Cathaysia—moderate; Euramerican—subtropical–tropical.
6. Each has its distinctive floristic provinces.
7. The Angara and the Cathaysia have more forms (structurally, not taxonomically) in common than they have with the other floras.
8. The flora of the Southern Hemisphere (Glossopteris) contrasts more with the floras of the Northern Hemisphere than the latter do with each other, structurally and taxonomically.

would be welcomed as a timely contribution by the palaeobotanists. Palaeomagnetism promises to have value in this respect.

The Legacy of Palaeomagnetism

Geophysical studies give plausibility to the idea that not only did the magnetic poles move on routes that are greatly longer than those experienced in modern times, but also the theory of permanence may not obtain.

According to Irving and Green (1957) to bring palaeomagnetic directions into conformity in the Southern Hemisphere the continents would have to be brought together to make a supercontinent. If this situation did in fact obtain, during pre-Tertiary times there would have been a supercontinent (Gondwanaland) at the position of the present South Pole. The components of the Glossopteris flora at present separated by oceans would then be in reasonable apposition and placed in proximity. In post-Miocene times on palaeomagnetic evidence there has been no appreciable shift in the position of the South Pole.

In the Carboniferous, the Equator, according to palaeomagnetic studies, would have crossed southern Europe and struck the North American coast south of Charlottetown to traverse the United States. The Carboniferous North Pole (Creer et al. 1957.) would have been slightly north of the Cathaysia flora and in the Angara flora. This is plausible palaeobotanically.

We may not yet be entirely satisfied, but palaeomagnetism has afforded improvement. Earlier attempts at relocating the poles were often highly subjective, for example the claim for polar relocation in which the Tertiary (Eocene) pole was estimated at being in the North Pacific 2000 miles west and a little south of Vancouver. For European palaeobotanists this was most satisfactory, for then Spitzbergen's Eocene flora would have flourished (which it did), but Arnold indicates (1947, p. 399) that this would have endowed Oregon with a climate incompatible with its Eocene flora. Chaney

(1940) states: "In taking care of their own Tertiary forests, certain Europeans have condemned ours to freezing." This observation was made in 1936. Obviously, the early evidence for polar wandering needed corroboration from palaeomagnetic observations.

If palaeomagnetic evidence is to be more helpful to the palaeobotanist, it must reveal continental patterns of drift that render accountable the present geographic locations of elements of the four great floras of Palaeozoic–Early Mesozoic times. It must provide an accounting for regional climatic phenomena that bear on floristic distribution.

Complex floras, more often than not, respond sluggishly, subtly, or only partially to climatic change in the context of geological time. In other words, floras may seem relatively stable in constitution and yet the climate may change (and by inference polar position). For instance, since the withdrawal of the last ice sheet from southern Ontario and the re-establishment of vegetal cover, the climate must have been moderate if the flora is regarded as the indicator. Yet, the fact that the edge of the ice cap is now some two to three thousand miles to the north must have made a significant change in climate. Plants as floras are highly adaptive to climatic generalization.

The post-Palaeozoic shift of North America with respect to the position of the Pole supports a conclusion that the uniform Euramerican flora became dissected and that the resulting change in climate was commensurate with the floral constitution before and after migration.

The Angara flora was not similarly disturbed and the major delineation of character maintained coherence, a condition which also persisted in the Cathaysia Complex. The Glossopteris flora, like the Euramerican, depicts constancy and the polar displacement, which apparently signifies drift, solves a palaeobotanical enigma. There is no satisfactory answer, or even hypothesis, explaining the wide separation of the land masses on which this uniformity is expressed. The striking difference between the Glossopteris and the Euramerican in terms of floral composition is so marked as to have led to the suggestion that if the northern complex was warm-loving, the southern one must have been cold-loving (Walton 1953, p. 146). Admixture of the two great floras was casual in Rhodesia (Walton). Walton augments this view with reference to the existence of the Permo-Carboniferous Ice Age.

The Interplay of Genetic and Adaptive Mechanisms

A second source of evidence may arise in botanical considerations to supplement the use of floras and what this term conveys.

The ability for living substance to evolve is primarily a function of genetic and hereditary phenomena. In terms of geological history it would be a very difficult task to estimate rates of evolution in any one interval of time, particularly when in plant fossils we so often lack significant organs. Also in a given taxon some organs or parts therof are very conservative and others develop complexities in structural and physiological detail.

Turning to environment, and the analysis of adaptivity and selection, let us consider the establishment of a successful morphological plant structure. One of the most significant events in the history of plants as portrayed by fossils is the development of leaves with massive venation, which in contrast to simple enations permits complex physiological activity. A more impressive development still is the evolution culminating in the seed habit. A third evolutionary process gave rise to the herbaceous habit.

The first-mentioned event, which culminated in the modern leaf, facilitated rapid energy build-up in large amounts in short intervals of daily time. This feature lends itself to vegetative expansion involving the production of enormous masses of protoplasm in an astonishingly short time. It is a feature that facilitates success in competition and storage of energy to cope with environmental adversity and limitation.

Seeds, representing another selected adaptive entity, afford effective propagation even if the parental source is obliterated by nature. They store energy, contain a whole plant, as it were, in miniature, can withstand drought and heat and cold, and require token amounts of oxygen to keep them alive until the day of germination. Their highest level of adaptive excellence is achieved in the modern gymnosperm and the angiosperm.

With the herbaceous trend, optimum dormancy in contemporary terms became a possibility. The aerial parts of the plant could die to ground level but persistent buds (or their equivalents) could regain high levels of biological efficiency when favourable conditions returned. Also, vegetative propagation and accompanying spread were greatly assisted, for example in the mosses. The trend exemplified by herbaceous plants was inherited largely by non-woody plants, but even woody ones achieved their level of success: the fig tree, for example, survives not only after leaf fall but also revives after winter die-back to the ground, a condition common on the coast of British Columbia in the present day.

Whatever the total effect of environment, these several fundamental advances have persisted and developed. They have not advanced equally, either with respect to time, geological period, or botanical taxon. Either genetic sluggishness or adaptive limitation (and therefore selection), or both, played their part in different ways and on a range of time differentials.

To derive from so complex a system anything conclusive is too much to expect. On the other hand, examination of Figure 5, in which an attempt is made to portray the factors of the system in graphic, summary form, facilitates the adopting of fresh perspective, which is both useful and perhaps helpfully suggestive. It represents an attempt to provide a new approach to the drift vs. permanence question on a basis other than the floristic one, which as seen from the most recent literature (cf. Axelrod 1963) presents contradictions.

The salient morphological trends (*vide* Fig. 5), drawn to show relative prominence in terms of time, must have an explanation not merely genetic. If this is not so, why did these changes not approach culmination during the

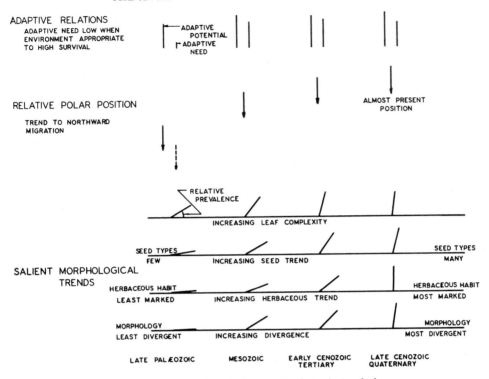

FIGURE 5. Northern Hemisphere, polar-botanical relations.

Carboniferous? Changed environmental conditions prevailing in subsequent intervals cannot be avoided as a reasonable answer.

Within the group of morphological trends examined, ability to build and store energy is the significant resulting biological achievement. The type of propagation and somatic development adopted through selection relates directly to environmental controls in which the need for dormancy is explicit.

The question as to what the environmental pressures were and which one or ones were limiting at given periods is the most significant one to ask. Geomorphic differentials, the effects of mountains and seas, must loom large in the answer even as they do for plants of the present day. Polar movement, if it occurred on a scale larger than it does now, would also be significant. One might well claim that drift (either as distinct from or related to polar wandering) would be equally significant, but it would depend upon where the land masses wandered with respect to the poles. Because the morphological trends (Fig. 5) apply universally (though not uniformly), the temptation to remove geomorphic control to a secondary level seems reasonable. Polar wandering and possibly drift then come to the foreground of consideration.

Palaeomagnetic studies, when applied to the present North American land mass, suggest changes in latitude in the proportions shown in Figure 5.

If this evidence is adopted, even approximately, the largest climatic disturbance would have occurred in Late Palaeozoic and into the Mesozoic, which is when the first major emphasis in morphological shift was evidenced by the plant world (*vide* depression reflected in sequence of polar symbols for this interval on Fig. 5). Adaptive need, as time went on, would increase if the poles moved in the manner indicated. The record of selection, in which the named morphological trends were emphasized, is consistent with adaptive response to these changes.

To the extent that these botanical developments conform to proposed polar positions derived through palaeomagnetic study, there is a logical claim that palaeobotanical events support palaeomagnetic findings.

SOME BOTANICAL OBJECTIONS TO CONTINENTAL DRIFT

Axelrod (1963) does not feel that there is any evidence derived from palaeofloristic study to support a contention that continents have drifted. He claims that, for example, the proposed shift of South Africa, which was centred, as claimed, over the South Pole in the Carboniferous, through 60 degrees of latitude in the proposed Permo-Triassic continental migration northward would induce considerable floristic change which is not actually in evidence. It would take strong geomorphic evidence to overcome Axelrod's objections. The Ice Age intervention, particularly since, as Andrews (1961) notes, it produced some ice apparently moving in a direction *from* the Equator, appears to make no contribution towards a solution of the dilemma.

Axelrod also objects to palaeomagnetic inferences because the Carboniferous position of the coal forests 10–20 degrees north of the Equator implies tropical conditions conforming with the view that the floras were in fact tropical, but the position of the flora of the Southern Hemisphere at the equivalent time must then also have been tropical because its coal flora were "very similar." This argument I find weaker than the first on the grounds that the late Palaeozoic flora in the south is generally in considerable contrast with its northern equivalent. It is true that there is a degree of sameness in the comparison, but there are marked secondary differences, for example, as shown in *Scutum* by Plumstead (1958) in Africa.

If one considers the great peat-forming areas of the modern world, though there are undoubtedly marked structural likenesses among the plant contributors to the peat, generally there are floristic differences. The "pegasse" of British Guiana is in floristic contrast to the peat accumulation at the mouth of the Niger, and peat accumulations near Leningrad contrast floristically with those on the Orkney Islands or near Fort Churchill, Manitoba, or in the Maritime Provinces of Canada. This is not to claim that Axelrod is wrong in assuming that the Carboniferous Coal Forests *must* be tropical, though as Arnold (1947) indicates, most of our present-day organic deposits are temperate. Just as there are many different kinds of peat (constitutionally), there were different kinds of coal. Arnold conveys a point that the mosses make the contrast between modern and ancient organic deposits. This is only partly true, for there is organic terrain in British Columbia constituted of massive logs in depth, a situation resembling the young Onakawana lignites of northern Ontario, where 30-foot depths are common.

One of Axelrod's basic assumptions in his objection to the drift hypothesis is that major floras are disposed in accordance with successional symmetry conforming to latitude. It is difficult to accept this *in toto*. The culminating flora of the organic terrain in Canada shows major structural and floristic differences often reflected in depth; these do not necessarily conform to latitude. Arnold (1947) emphasizes the importance of geomorphic inference, not latitude, in accounting for floristic distribution. A high water table and proximity to the sea make for broad constitution in the related flora. Also, environmental combinations overshadow latitude implications often significantly to the point where primary morphological entities remain faithful to type as in sedge peat-cover, which is similar from 400 miles south of the present geographic North Pole to a position 40 degrees north in latitude.

I am hopeful that Axelrod will qualify his views on the primary significance of his insistence on this symmetry factor in relation to latitude, particularly when in another account he claims (Axelrod 1952, pp. 51–52): "Cain (1944, p. 75) has pointed out that breadfruit (*Artocarpus*), which is now strictly tropical, and which has been recorded at higher latitudes, may have been represented in Cretaceous and Early Tertiary floras by one or more temperate to warm temperate species as in the case of certain genera today, such as persimmon (*Diospyros*), avocado (*Persea*) and magnolia (*Magnolia*)." We may add in this connection that a number of genera that are frequently regarded as temperate, such as alder (*Alnus*), maple (*Acer*), birch (*Betula*), haw (*Crataegus*), katsura (*Cercidophyllum*), sweet gum (*Liquidambar*), and sycamore (*Platanus*), were widely represented in the warm temperate to subtropical zone during the Cretaceous and Early Tertiary. Pertinently, many of the widely distributed families in the Northern Hemisphere that are often considered as temperate, including the Aceraceae, Betulaceae, Fagaceae, Rosaceae, Ulmaceae, and others, extend into the tropics. The most primitive living species of maple, poplar, birch, oak, cherry, and hackberry are largely evergreen types, and are found in warm temperate to tropical regions.

Axelrod, in his claims supporting the permanence hypothesis, emphasizes the importance of large leaves for the characterization of tropical plants in contrast to small leaves for temperate ones. This observation has questionable application to modern times. Plants with large leaves at the tropics today are predominantly angiosperm, whereas in the Carboniferous angiosperm were non-existent. Thus, the production of large-leaved plants is fundamentally a genetic function with selection following. A genetic mechanism, despite climate, produced the Glossopteris large-leaved types. They too were secondarily selected. Climate did not "induce" their evolution.

In fairness to those faithful to the idea of continental drift, I must side with Chaloner and move with the palaeobotanists who welcome the new support for this theory, which encourages us to look again at the organization of our plant fossil record.

THE WILSON RECONSTRUCTION MECHANISM

If drift as a hypothesis is to be accepted by palaeobotanists, the mechanism is bound to be involved because it gives the location of isolated activity in the drift system, a circumstance useful in the provision of palaeobotanical examples. Wilson, in this volume, points out the significance of the mid-ocean ridges.

The trans-Atlantic connection recognized in the Cabot fault that traverses Newfoundland and parts of Nova Scotia offers a basis for palaeobotanical conjecture. Both macro- and micro-fossil studies already begun (Radforth and Walton 1960) for the Carboniferous Minto flora may now be aligned for comparative study with Carboniferous rocks of Scotland. Likeness between the floras of east and west on a morphological basis (not necessarily, as yet, floristically) is in evidence, and it is perhaps not surprising that there would be similarity. Details of any possible relationship will, it is hoped, be worked out in continued investigations of the author and his Scottish colleague, whose first work was done before knowledge of Wilson's proposed trans-Atlantic connection existed.

In the meantime the writer has been impressed by the sight of the great Wegener fault at Robeson Channel, which separates northern Greenland from Ellesmere Island, in explorations during visits to Ellesmere Island in two successive summers, 1962–63. With the assistance of Davies and Brideaux, the writer engaged in detailed studies of both Palaeozoic and Mesozoic micro- and macro-flora of Ellesmere Island. The Devonian macrofossils are comprised of stems, leaves, and fructifications of the *Archaeopteris* sp. from sites rediscovered by Andrews, Phillips, and the writer. Material, presumably from one of these locations, had been described by Nathorst at the turn of the century, but adequate techniques were then not available for palaeobotanical analysis.

A summary of the results with *Archaeopteris* indicates a homosporous condition and close vegetative resemblance to *A. hibernica* in Ireland.

One cannot tell whether the apparent ends of the Great Glen fault and the Cabot fault as they occur on land were at one time joined. There may be a considerable extension under the Atlantic Ocean. In any case as matters stand the relationship between the Ellesmere and Irish *Archaeopteris* is as close botanically as is that between the Irish and the European—for example Belgian *Archaeopteris*—if not closer.

An objection to this proposed trans-Atlantic alliance arises from the work of Arnold (1947) in which a heterosporous species of *Archaeopteris* was discovered in the Devonian of Pennsylvania. There are no known heterosporous species in Europe or elsewhere. One may argue therefore that the Pennsylvanian *Archaeopteris* favours the permanence of continental position. Had the Ellesmere Island *Archaeopteris* been heterosporous, this conclusion would have been hard to refute, but in the circumstances with homospory in the north and heterospory some 4000 miles to the south in a continental environment, the tentative conclusion must be that the heterosporous state represents the effect of local selection. This idea is strengthened when it is realized that the homosporous *Archaeopteris* of Ireland and Belgium, like the Ellesmere *Archaeopteris*, also enjoyed a marine environment. Also, Ireland is at present nearer to Ellesmere than to Pennsylvania.

When attention is turned to trans-Atlantic Devonian microfossils, it is found in our laboratory (Brideaux 1964), from comparisons of sources of Devonian spore identification made principally by Chaloner (1959), McGregor, and Naumova with evidence from other literature, that certain compilation of them is pertinent to the question of the intercontinental floral relationship. Thirteen genera of microfossils (probably more) are common to both the North American and European Devonian. Eight species are common. Several others show similarity. There is enough resemblance between microfossils of the Canadian Devonian and those of the Eurasian Devonian to form a hypothesis favouring the idea of late Devonian –early Carboniferous continental contiguity.* With contiguity effected, botanical intercontinental contamination would be expected thereafter, but divergence would inevitably ensue for reasons that have been discussed earlier. Therefore it is possible to find both similarity and dissimilarity in vegetal cover between separated continents, as one does today between North America and Europe. Where there is similarity, there would in all likelihood have been major differences at the times when similarity occurred.

It is a striking fact that Rouse (1956) has illustrated this very phenomenon in his study of transoceanic comparisons of Mesozoic microfossils, though he was not concerned at the time with the thought of continental drift. Although Wilson and Webster (1946) do not report similarities between European and American Mesozoic microfossils (which would favour Mesozoic separation of continents in any case), Rouse does. The latter found twelve distinct cases of microfossil similarity between Europe and North America in the Upper Mesozoic. Five forms present in Rouse's American assemblage have been found in younger Mesozoic of Europe and three in older.

In 1963 the writer, with Andrews and Phillips, discovered a new location on Ellesmere Island at which what are almost certainly Mesozoic macrofossils occur. At least five species (an example of one is shown in Fig. 6) occur as compressions. About five miles away from this location about 150 lb of petrified wood and at least one fruit the size and shape of a prune were discovered.

*That recent investigations have shown this relationship to be more complex does not invalidate this general statement.

FIGURE 6. A carbonaceous compression of a fertile pinna segment (*Phlebopteris angustiloba*, probably Jurassic (Hirmer and Hoerhammer)): Mesozoic Ellesmere Island. From Davies (1965).

The entire complex bears some resemblance to the plants of the Potomac in the Early Cretaceous of Maryland, but the taxa on which this comparison is made are major ones involving ferns, cycadophytes, conifers, and possibly pteridosperms. If comparison involves generic and specific features, it must be suggested that divergence prevailed. However, this divergence is not so marked as it is between the Ellesmere Mesozoic examples and those of western Greenland. By the close of the Mesozoic, one might expect wide divergence, but the independence exhibited between Ellesmere Island and Greenland in this respect is more marked than that between Greenland and Great Britain. The existence of the Wegener fault appears to explain the divergence in part. It will be useful to learn what future microfossil studies will divulge on this subject.

In the meantime the north-south axial alliance is supported by such claims as that of Arnold (1947, p. 398) that the sequoias (Tertiary) migrated from Alaska to their present location in the southern portion of the western North American coast; this, despite the fact that *Sequoia* has not been able to migrate from the western mainland to adjacent islands in recent times (Chaney, 1940, p. 477).

The eastern Greenland Rhaetic floras (Harris 1938) and the younger Lower Cretaceous western Greenland Complex of undoubted angiosperms, including *Artocarpus* (breadfruit tree) and magnolias, might have left their legacy to the south via Europe (Walton 1953, p. 177). This would have been accomplished before the proposed opening of the Atlantic Ocean slightly prior to the onset of the Cretaceous. The timing would be appropriate because the Greenland flora was already advanced by then, and relics of angiosperms and their associates could have been disseminated southeasterly.

In any case the observations based on the Devonian and Mesozoic using Ellesmere Island as the focal point of interest suggest that there was, prior to the Carboniferous, contiguity of lands of the Eastern and Western hemispheres. During the Mesozoic, while uniformity could be exhibited based on microfossils, this and the observations contrasting the macrofloral constitution of the northern continents conform to the later separation to secondary continents. The Ellesmere Island palaeobotanical complex (Devonian as pre-drift and late Mesozoic as post-drift) will remain a central feature in these studies.

The mechanism of convection and associated crustal separation provides time-differentials, appropriate directions, and separation times that suit the palaeobotanical requirements as reasoned here, but this reasoning is not claimed to be conclusive. In addition, the analysis tentatively favours polar wandering as derived from palaeomagnetic studies and (despite the objection of Axelrod 1963) conforms with the idea of drift as opposed to permanence sufficiently to allow it to stand as a hypothesis for further investigation.

REFERENCES

ANDREWS, H. N. (1961). Studies in Palaeobotany. New York: John Wiley and Sons, Inc.

ARNOLD, C. A. (1947). An Introduction to Palaeobotany. New York: McGraw-Hill Book Co., Inc.

AXELROD, D. I. (1952). A theory of Angiosperm evolution. Evolution, 6 (I): 29–60.

———— (1963). Fossil floras. Suggest stable not drifting continent. J. Geophys. Res., 68 (10): 14, 3257–3263.

BRIDEAUX, W. W. (1964). Laboratory notes. Unpublished.

CAIN, S. A. (1944). Foundations of Plant Geography. New York: Harper and Bros.

CHALONER, W. G. (1959). Continental Drift. New Biology (Penguin Books), No. 29: 7–30.

CHANEY, R. W. (1940). Tertiary forests and continental history. Geol. Soc. Amer. Bull., 51: 469–488.

CREER, K. M., IRVING, E., and RUNCORN, S. K. (1957). Palaeomagnetic investigations in Great Britain, VI. Geophysical interpretation of palaeomagnetic directions from Great Britain. Phil. Trans. Roy. Soc. (London), Ser. A, 250: 144–156.

DAVIES, P. G. (1965). A Mesozoic Fossil Flora from Arctic Ellesmere Island. MSc Thesis, McMaster University, Hamilton, Ontario.

HALLE, T. G. (1937). On the relation between the Late Paleozoic floras of Eastern and Northern Asia. Deux. Congress. Strat. Carbonifere Heerlen, *1*: 237–245.

HARRIS, T. M. (1938). The British Rhaetic Flora. Brit. Mus. Nat. Hist.: 1–8.

IRVING, E. and GREEN, R. (1957). Palaeomagnetic evidence from the Cretaceous and Cainozoic. Nature, *179*: 1064–1065.

KRISHNAN, M. S. (1954). History of the Gondwana Era in Relation to the Distribution and Development of Flora. Seward Memorial Lecture, Sahni Inst. of Palaeobotanists, Lucknow: 1–15.

KOLBE, R. W. (1957). Fresh-water diatoms from Atlantic deep-sea sediments. Science, *126*: 1053–1056.

PLUMSTEAD, E. P. (1958). The habit of growth of Glossopteridae. Trans. Geol. Soc. South Africa, *61*: 81–94.

NEUBERG, M. F. (1955). New representatives of the Lower Permian Angara Flora. Dokl. Akad. Nauk SSSR, *102* (2): 613–616.

ROUSE, G. E. (1956). The Disclosure and Palaeobotanical Evaluation of Plant Microfossils from Selected Cretaceous Coal-Bearing Strata of Canada. Ph.D. Thesis, McMaster University, Hamilton, Ontario.

SAHNI, B. (1936). Wegener's theory of continental drift in the light of Palaeobotanical evidence. J. Indian Bot. Soc., *15* (5): 319–332.

STUBBS, P. (1964). Taking continental drift seriously. New Scientist, *21* (384): 800–803.

RADFORTH, N. W. and WILKINSON, L. (1959). The significance of plant microfossils found in Canadian Devonian rocks. Trans. Roy. Soc. Can., Ser. III, Sec. V, *53*: 29–34.

RADFORTH, N. W. and WALTON, J. (1960). On some fossil plants from the Minto Coalfield, New Brunswick. Senck. leth., *41* (1/6): 101–119.

WALTON, J. (1953). An Introduction to the Study of Fossil Plants, 2nd ed. London: Adam and Charles Black.

WILSON, L. R. and WEBSTER, R. M. (1946). Plant microfossils from a Fort Union coal of Montana. Amer. J. of Bot., *33* (4): 271–278.

ASTRONOMICAL EVIDENCE ON THE
PRESENT RATE OF CONTINENTAL DRIFT

R. W. Tanner

SINCE AN ASTRONOMER may give the latitude and longitude of his station to one hundredth of a second of arc, corresponding to about 30 cm on the earth's surface, it seems reasonable to ask him what evidence there is of relative motion of continents at the present time. On the face of it, half a century of such observations in Europe and America, say, should suffice to determine whether or not drifts of the order of one centimeter per year are now occurring between these continents. But there is almost as much argument over the interpretation of such observations as there is over continental drift itself. I propose to follow the interpretation of Markowitz of the U.S. Naval Observatory and to explain some of the matters of controversy. These understood, we may examine the prospects for future improvement in the astronomical determination of relative continental positions.

To begin almost at the beginning, when two observers have located their zeniths and the pole of rotation of the earth among the stars, the arc zenith-pole is the complement of the latitude, and the angle at the pole between the arcs is the difference in longitude. The zenith corresponds to the outward normal to the geoid and the pole to the centre of the diurnal arcs of the stars. Direct measurement of latitude and longitude on this principle runs into difficulties: the stars' directions in a fixed co-ordinate system are not completely invariable; the pole of rotation is fixed neither among them nor in the body of the earth; large angles have to be measured with large corrections for refraction and smaller ones for flexure, divided circle errors, and so on. If all these complications occur together, the results are generally useless for our purpose. For example, the classic meridian circle programme for the determination of star positions gives as a by-product the mean latitude of the instrument for the epoch of the programme, but our Ottawa experience agrees with that of others in finding differences up to several tenths of a second of arc from programme to programme having little or nothing to do with real changes in latitude. More specialized instruments are necessary.

Three instruments that avoid the measurement of large angles are in general use, the zenith telescope, the photographic zenith tube (PZT), and the prism astrolabe (in the Danjon modification). The zenith telescope observes pairs of stars of nearly equal north and south zenith distances at transit with reversal of the instrument about a vertical axis between the two stars. The small difference in zenith distance is the principal measured quantity, and the latitude is equal to the mean of the declination of the two stars corrected by one half the measured difference. The PZT repeatedly photographs single stars close to the zenith with lens and photographic plate reversed as a unit several times about the vertical. Latitude again depends mainly on the measured zenith distance and the declination, and with the addition of clock timing of the plate drive the local sidereal time is also found so that longitudes may be deduced as well. The astrolabe observes the instant at which a star has a zenith distance of 30°: by choosing stars of known position in various azimuths both latitudes and time are determined.

Each instrument has its vices and virtues; I shall dwell on those of the PZT which are familiar to me and possibly less known to you than those of the standard zenith telescope. The PZT works with only a narrow zone of fainter stars whose absolute co-ordinates it cannot determine; very few of these stars are in the fundamental catalogues of precision, so that a special study of their positions and motions has to be undertaken before the results can be compared with another instrument's. Vigilant care is required to ensure the continuous fulfilment of the geometric conditions assumed. It is notorious that some PZT's will sometimes give results systematically wrong by several tenths of a second of arc for weeks or months; two such anomalous periods at Ottawa were ended when the objective was found to be loose in its cell. In 1960 the Ottawa instrument was moved about a hundred metres into a special hut with a more favourable "microclimate," with a consequent sharp reduction in our accidental errors, but there is a suspicion that we also introduced a discontinuity in our longitude several metres different from the change on the ground. On the credit side the PZT has a minimum of refraction to contend with; the scale is larger (but one micron on the plate still amounts to a metre and a half on the ground), and its impersonal automatic observations are an important consideration, especially in our winter climate.

To turn now to the least unsatisfactory results secured with such instruments: the International Latitude Service (ILS) has had a chain of five zenith telescopes around the world in latitude 39° 08′ N in practically continuous operation since the end of the last century, employing common lists of stars and common techniques. A minutely detailed path of polar motion is revealed, but the final distillation of over a million observations, as far as we are concerned, is, according to Markowitz (1960), that the observed latitudes can be accounted for completely by polar motion plus errors of observation. The largest residual from the polar motion solution for any one of five stations (in mean latitude, for any one of the seven 6–12 year intervals considered) is only 0.024″. The stations appear to have been fixed with respect to the earth as a whole within about 0.01″ over a half century. Therefore secular motions in the north-south direction appear to be less than about one centimeter per year at present.

The evidence on longitude changes is much less satisfactory. The ILS stations do not determine longitudes, and the other two instruments began to come into general use only in the 1950's. Millisecond accuracy in time (corresponding to 0.01″ in our latitudes) is also a comparatively recent development. The mean errors in longitude for the three most recent world longitude programmes were: 1926, 27 msec.; 1933, 17 msec.; 1957.5–60 IGY period), 3 msec. This material is deplorably inhomogeneous; the results of established time services at the larger fixed observatories are less so and have long been recorded by the Bureau Internationale de l'Heure (BIH). Markowitz' (1960) analysis of the BIH results during 1934–55 obtained at Europe and Washington, after substantial correction of the latter's time for errors in the proper motions of the PZT stars, shows no relative motion, but his estimate of the probable error is 0.015″ per year. That is, east–west motions up to half a metre a year could not be excluded.

The geophysicist concerned with continental drift is likely to find this evidence inconclusive. What are the prospects for improvement? The methods described involve such a complex of variables in addition to possible station movements that progress is likely to be slow. Some hopeful developments are: the continuation of the ILS programme, supplemented with other zenith telescopes, PZT's, and astrolabes, by the new International Polar Motion Service (IPMS); improvements in the fundamental catalogue and its extension to fainter stars; observations in progress or planned for the tying together of the various PZT catalogues into the fundamental system; the possibility that two or more PZT's in the same latitude will use common stars (Washington and Mizusawa, for example, have 40 common stars); the installing of more instruments in the Southern Hemisphere; the operation of two or more types of instrument at the same station over extended periods, and the careful planning of observing programmes with regard to secular effects.

If we are still unhappy at these prospects, what can be expected of other astronomical methods of position determination? Occultations, eclipses, and moon camera programmes involving our natural satellite are not promising in this respect. The moon has given many astronomers headaches since Newton; station co-ordinates at any one epoch, though largely freed of reference to the local vertical, are likely to remain uncertain by tens of metres at best.

Artificial satellites offer the possibility of bridging the oceans by an extension of the geodesist's triangulation methods, and I shall conclude by speaking a little about their application to our problem from the astronomical point of view. It seems best at present to avoid dealing with the dynamics of the satellite's motion by making the observations simultaneous or nearly so. If simultaneity is assured by having the satellite flash, a large number of flashes are required to average out the "seeing" disturbances; if the averaging is accomplished by using many points along the trailed image against the stellar background, millisecond timing of the shutter breaks is necessary. The opportunities for observation are limited by time and weather. Despite these limitations, the Smithsonian stations in the Americas, for example, have had the lines joining them located to about 1″ in azimuth from a few tens of pairs of simultaneous observations, and the United States Coast and Geodetic Survey has recently succeeded in getting relative intracontinental locations to about 1 metre using Echo and Anna. Other agencies are active in this field, and we may expect to have a dozen or more points around the earth located to something like 1 metre accuracy in a pretty rigorously defined rectangular co-ordinate system inside a decade. Even so, more decades must elapse before astronomical methods can speak with certainty of one centimeter a year.

REFERENCE

MARKOWITZ, W. (1960). The secular motion of the pole. *In* Methods and Techniques in Geophysics, edited by S. K. Runcorn, pp. 325–361. New York: Interscience Publishers Inc.

PART II

Evidence on Continental Drift from the Arctic
and Eastern Seaboard of Canada

DEVELOPMENT OF SUBMARINE PHYSIOGRAPHY IN THE CANADIAN ARCTIC AND ITS RELATION TO CRUSTAL MOVEMENTS

B. R. Pelletier

THIS REPORT deals primarily with the development of submarine physiography in the Canadian Arctic (Fig. 1), and is based on the hypothesis of Fortier and Morley (1956) that the Arctic Archipelago is a geological unity and that the network of inter-island channels is a submerged river

FIGURE 1. Index Map.

system of Tertiary age, which previously drained a continuous land mass (Fig. 2). The new soundings, and the palaeontological and lithological evidence obtained with bottom grabbers and cores, offer additional support to the general theory of subaerial erosion of a pre-existing single land mass by streams. Certain lines of topographic evidence indicate that modification of such river valleys by valley glaciers also took place (Pelletier 1961, 1962, 1963; Horn, 1963) and was followed by widespread submergence. This submergence was followed by an interval of post-Pleistocene emergence, according to the comprehensive study of relict strand lines and raised marine deposits carried out by Craig and Fyles (1960). This emergence may be continuing although the gravity data of Sobczak (1963) tentatively indicate that the western part of the Archipelago and adjacent continental shelf may be in isostatic equilibrium.

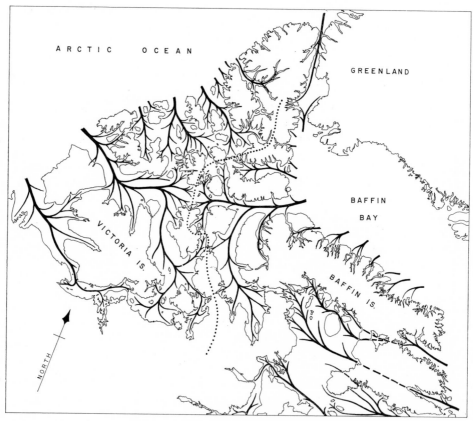

INFERRED SUBMERGED TERTIARY DRAINAGE SYSTEM

AFTER Y.O.FORTIER AND L.W.MORLEY, ROY. SOC. CAN., VOL. L, SER. 3, JUNE, 1956.

MAIN DIVIDE ·············

0   150   300   MILES

FIGURE 2. Tertiary drainage system. Note the major watershed passing down from north to south through the central part of the islands.

Acknowledgments

The writer wishes to thank his many associates on the Canadian Polar Continental Shelf Project who gave willingly of their time and effort in affording logistic support and material aid in the undertaking of the studies carried out over the Arctic Ocean: E. F. Roots, the co-ordinator; F. DuVernet, the former field supervisor, now deceased; C. Grant, the present supervisor; field officers of the Department of Mines and Technical Surveys, particularly the Project's former oceanographer A. E. Collin, the senior hydrographer R. M. Eaton, surveyor F. H. Hunt, and geologists D. R. Horn and G. Vilks. Special mention is made of the crews of Autair Helicopters Limited of Montreal, Quebec, and McMurray Air Services Limited of Uranium City, Saskatchewan, who carried out the assignments of landing parties on hundreds of unprepared landing areas on the Archipelago itself, and on the ice of the Arctic Ocean. The writer owes his thanks to Captain N. V. Clark of the icebreaker C.C.G.S. "Labrador," and her officers and men who offered the writer every assistance during an oceanographic cruise in the autumn of 1963 into Baffin Bay, Jones Sound, and Nares Strait as far north as Hall Basin.

On the sampling operations over the Arctic Ocean, the writer was assisted by his present departmental associates: K. Abbot-Smith, A. E. Collin, D. R. Horn, R. Lahey, E. L. Lewis, E. W. Reinhardt, and G. Vilks. On the cruise of the "Labrador" some of the writer's past associates such as R. Cooper, J. Y. Dugas, T. Lee, P. H. McGrath, and D. Snodgrass were of considerable help in obtaining geological, geophysical, and oceanographic data. In the laboratory, bottom samples were processed by R. Cormier, while some of the illustrations were prepared by Miss Sonia Pitcher, Miss Penny Wise, and Mr. Alan Grant. The writer especially thanks his colleagues Dr. A. E. Collin, Dr. L. H. King, and Dr. R. J. Leslie for the many valuable suggestions they made in their critical reading of the manuscript. Finally acknowledgment is made to Y. O. Fortier and L. W. Morley of the Geological Survey of Canada, whose original work led the writer to develop further their hypothesis upon which this report is based.

Previous Work

Early explorers and investigators such as Nansen, Peary, Stefanssen, and Sverdrup made fundamental contributions to studies of arctic waters and the floors beneath them during the latter part of the nineteenth century and the early decades of this century. This work was followed by the hydrographic studies of the Russian investigators commencing around 1930 when their ships penetrated many parts of the ice-covered Arctic Ocean. In 1937 the Russian oceanographic work was extended to the central part of the Arctic Ocean by means of aircraft. With this support, camps were established on the ice and occupied for periods of several months. Much of this early work, which also involved geological and geophysical investigations, is discussed by Ostenso (1962) and Collin and Dunbar (1964).

In recent years submarine physiography in the Canadian Arctic has been studied by technical teams from the Department of Mines and Technical Surveys, Ottawa, under the co-ordination of the Polar Continental Shelf Project, the Marine Sciences Branch, and in particular the Bedford Institute of Oceanography at Dartmouth, Nova Scotia, and the Geological Survey of Canada. Other investigators include those of the Fisheries Research Board of Canada, the Arctic Institute of North America, the Defence Research Board of Canada, the United States Air Force Cambridge Research Centre (particularly the programme on the Ice Island T-3 over the Arctic Ocean), the Department of Transport, and many other domestic and foreign institutions. The work of these groups, which is rather closely related to the study area, is covered by publications of Hunkins et al. (1960), Collin (1961), Eaton (1961), Perry (1961), Pelletier (1961, 1962, 1963), Wagner (1962, 1964), Buckley (1963), Horn (1963), Manchester (1964), Marlowe and Vilks (1963), Marlowe (1964), and Vilks (1964).

The Western Channels and Adjacent Continental Shelf

The submarine physiography of the western channels and adjacent continental shelf is described by Collin (1961), Pelletier (1961, 1962, 1963), Horn (1963), Marlowe and Vilks (1963), and Vilks (1964). The data from these investigations indicate that an unusual, or complex, physiographic development has taken place and that problems of crustal movement, glaciation, and changes in sea level are intimately involved. In connection with these inferences the most striking observations made were those on the submarine area immediately adjacent to Borden, Ellef Ringnes, Meighen, and Axel Heiberg islands. Along the channels separating these islands, the bottom profile is steep close to shore, and only a few miles off shore, depths of 450 to 550 metres occur (Figs. 3 and 4). Such depths are more than twice that of the continental shelves (187 metres) in most parts of the world, although some shelves have now been redefined and are about 500 metres deep (Shepard 1963).

In contrast to these excessive depths in the channels, the depths of water off the seaward tips of the islands adjacent to the Arctic Ocean are small (Figs. 3 and 4). Here the bottom slopes gently in a northwesterly direction. This gentle slope, which begins at the tip of the low-lying headlands, is broken by a series of short, steep slopes a few metres or tens of metres in height. Continuing seaward this slope assumes an almost horizontal attitude about 40 to 60 miles off shore at a depth of 400 to 450 metres. The continental shelf is thought to extend to the next marked break in profile at a depth of 650 metres at a point 110 miles off shore (Figs. 3 and 4). Because the depth over the inner continental shelf is the same as that over much of the inland channels, and because the topography of these two major

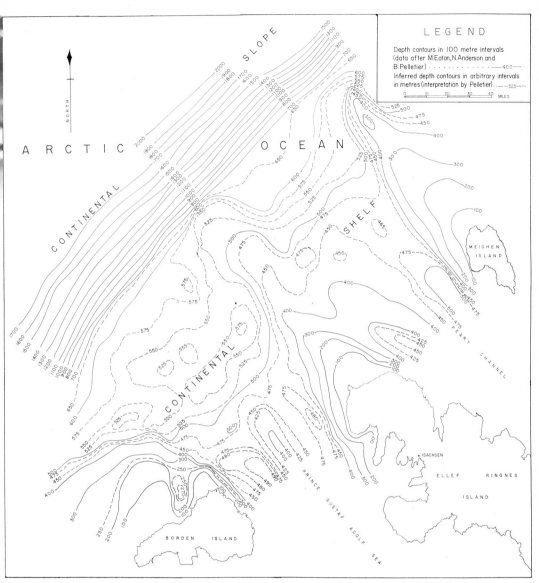

FIGURE 3. Physiography of the arctic continental shelf and adjacent channels. The dominant physical influence of the headlands protruding on to the continental shelf is evident; also the steep submarine valleys, which are characterized by median ridges and terminated seaward by hummocky terrain thought to be moraines. Topography seaward of the islands is gentle, but on the channel sides is steep.

areas is contrasting, the inference was reached that the entire Arctic region had a complex physiographic history.

To obtain a clearer idea of the nature of this complex physiographic development, several topographic profiles were drawn. The transverse profile of Peary Channel, as well as that of Prince Gustaf Adolf Sea, is

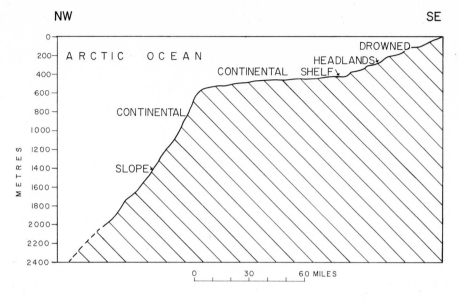

(a) CONTINENTAL SHELF AND SLOPE

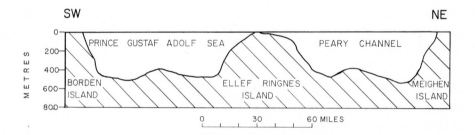

(b) ADJACENT ARCTIC CHANNELS

FIGURE 4. Physiography profiles of the Arctic continental shelf and adjacent channels. In the lower figure U-shaped valleys and medium ridges of the two main troughs are evident.

that of a broad U-shaped valley interrupted by a median rise extending along the axis of the channel (Figs. 3 and 4). In these transverse profiles the rises begin at depths up to 100 metres above the general level of the channel floors, and rise towards the southeast, where they terminate as islands. The relatively deep troughs forming the channel floors on either side of the submerged median ridges are thought to be the original, though modified, river valleys of a dendritic pattern of streams that drained the area when the land stood higher relative to sea-level. Thus the simple picture of a single submerged river valley is not entirely correct, although the hypothesis of Fortier and Morley generally stands.

The floors of the main troughs are somewhat hummocky with small disconnected basins occurring along the entire length. In some cases these basins have the configuration of cirques, especially near the eastern ends of the troughs, and in other cases the basins resemble a system of paternoster lakes (personal communication, D. R. Horn, Geological Survey of Canada) such as occur in glaciated river valleys. Along this irregular bottom, a gradual increase in elevation takes place in the seaward direction. This increase in elevation takes the form of a "toeing-up" as the channel floors rise to the level of the continental shelf about 40 to 50 miles seaward of the western entrance to the inter-island channels. Here the troughs end in a series of transverse hummocky ridges, and form submerged sills about 25 to 50 metres in height. Because of the transverse nature of their position relative to the troughs, and because they occur at the "toed-up" end of the long U-shaped troughs, these ridges are thought to be terminal moraines of valley glaciers that advanced down the pre-Pleistocene drainage system and modified the river valleys into their present physiographic configuration.

In accordance with this theory of glacially modified fluvial valleys, it appears that submarine tributaries leading to the main troughs have also undergone modification by the action of valley glaciers. For instance, the walls of the main troughs are steep and regular but are broken by the entrance of submarine tributaries, which also are U-shaped in profile and hang approximately 100 to 200 metres above the floor of the main troughs. This unified pattern of submarine troughs and their tributaries is thought to represent the drainage system that existed in pre-Pleistocene times and was subsequently modified by the action of valley glaciers.

Although the general theory that the channels are the submerged remnants of an earlier drainage system appears plausible, the idea that the river valleys extended directly to the Arctic Ocean is not entirely correct as shown by the bathymetry of both Wilkins and Ballantyne straits (Fig. 5). Here bottom samples, which were obtained from the seaward side of these straits at depths of less than 175 metres, consist of black anaerobic mud. This indicates a lack of circulation and, possibly, non-passage of sea water entering these western channels at depths as shallow as 175 m and perhaps less. The barrier inhibiting this flow was thought to be physical, and this was confirmed when shallow soundings of less than 50 metres were recorded in several locations at the western end of both Wilkins and Ballantyne straits. From such observations it was concluded that, unlike the deeply submerged valleys comprising the bottom of Peary Channel and Prince Gustaf Adolf Sea, the floors of Wilkins and Ballantyne straits do not extend from the east directly to the Arctic Ocean, but have a submarine ridge separating the Arctic Ocean portion of their floors from the inland channel. This ridge extends between Borden and Brock islands, and continues southwesterly between Brock and Prince Patrick islands. It appears to have acted as a watershed from which rivers on the west side drained directly to the Arctic Ocean. On the east side of this ridge, however, water was

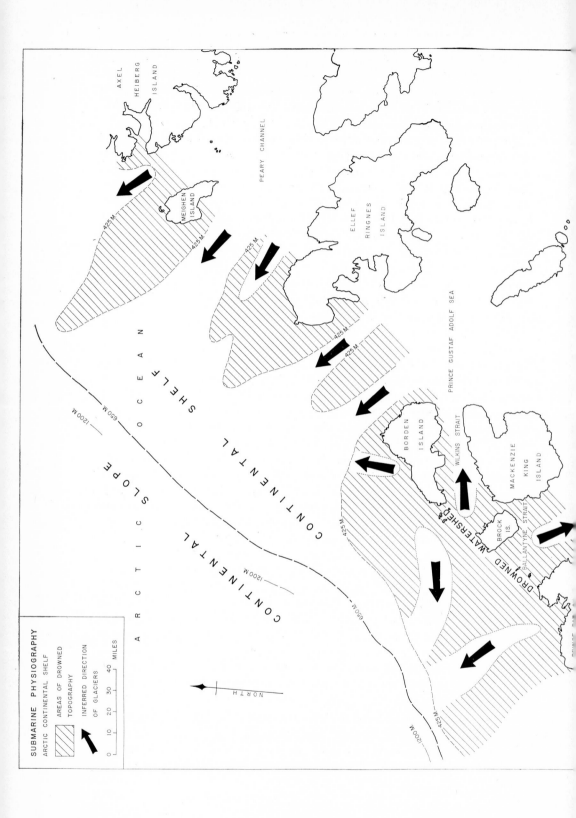

SUBMARINE PHYSIOGRAPHY

ARCTIC CONTINENTAL SHELF

▨ AREAS OF DROWNED
TOPOGRAPHY

➤ INFERRED DIRECTION
OF GLACIERS

0 10 20 30 40 MILES

NORTH

AXEL
HEIBERG
ISLAND

PEARY CHANNEL

MEIGHEN
ISLAND

ELLEF
RINGNES
ISLAND

PRINCE GUSTAF ADOLF SEA

ARCTIC OCEAN

CONTINENTAL SHELF

CONTINENTAL SLOPE

425 M

425 M

425 M

425 M

425 M

425 M

650 M

650 M

1200 M

1200 M

1200 M

650 M

BORDEN
ISLAND

WILKINS STRAIT

MACKENZIE
KING
ISLAND

BROCK
IS.

BALLANTYNE STRAIT

DROWNED WATERSHED

drained indirectly to the sea by means of a dendritic trunk system leading to the main channels that terminated along the former coast of the Arctic Ocean. Along these submerged river systems, both east and west of the drowned watershed, valley glaciation occurred, which subsequently modified the topography of the river valleys.

The evidence of such glaciation is gathered from an over-all consideration of the physical features both below and above sea level. This evidence is as follows: the U-shaped transverse profiles of the inter-island channels; hanging U-shaped valleys above the floors of the main channels or valleys; the presence of a hummocky terrain in the troughs; the possibility that the longitudinal series of basins in the troughs may be paternoster lakes; cirque-like features in the upland portion of the troughs and tributaries, some of which are submerged; the presence of ice-caps at the headward portion of some of the tributaries; and the longitudinal profile of the floors of the main channels, which exhibit a "toeing-up" in the seaward direction together with the possibility of terminal moraines on the floor of the Arctic Ocean at the seaward end of these main channels.

Estimates of the thickness of the lobes of ice responsible for the valley glaciation are based on the height of submerged terraces above the channel floors, and the difference in local relief of the so-called drowned cirques and the adjacent submerged coastal area. It appears that tongues of ice at least 1000 feet thick moved from ice-caps on the upland portions of the islands, through the fluvial valleys where they commonly merged with other tongues of ice and flowed seaward, where they terminated in the coastal waters of the Arctic Ocean (Fig. 5). Some glaciers appear to have headed on islands adjacent to the sea, and moved directly seaward. This may have been the case on the western part of Prince Patrick, Brock, Borden, and Axel Heiberg islands. Here the cirques open towards the continental shelf at various points 20 to 40 miles off shore, and are considered to be submerged, subaerially formed, topographic features.

It is possible that a thin sheet of ice eroded the land between the river valleys, but evidence of this glaciation is not substantial. However, any evidence that did occur on the islands may have been obliterated by wave action during a period of a higher stand of sea-level and subsequent marine regression. The fact that sinous ridges of sand occur at low elevations and are thought to be eskers (St. Onge 1964) is reason to suspect that some continental glaciation in the form of sheets of ice moved across the Arctic Islands. Further support to this theory is the occurrence of isolated boulders thought to be glacial erratics which occur at various elevations. It must be stressed, however, that if an ice-sheet did exist it must have been thinner

FIGURE 5. Interpretation of arctic physiographic events. Deep troughs separated by median ridges in main channels are evident; also the drowned watershed and the wide area of deep submergence. The limit of the continental slope is consistently 80–110 miles off shore; the outer continental shelf varies in width because of this submergence of drowned headlands and other topographic features.

than the valley lobes because there is no physiographic evidence comparable in magnitude to the features impressed by the action of valley glaciers.

Estimates on the amount of present submergence are based on the depth of occurrence of the following: terminal moraines, deep troughs, a pronounced submarine topographic nick on the seaward portion of the island headlands, and terraces flanking the channel sides of the islands. The terraces are at shallower depths in the inland portion of the channels than in the oceanic portion, thus indicating that the present submergence is greatest in the area of the terminal moraines and the northwestern most extension of the drowned headlands. In this latter area it amounts to more than 400 metres—and perhaps 440 to 450 metres would be a better approximation. Such drowning took place off shore to various distances up to 50 miles, where submerged headlands protrude upon the continental shelf. These drowned areas are shown in Figure 5, and the topographic influence of the headlands on the arctic continental shelf is shown further in Figure 3.

Other evidence for drowning in the Arctic Islands is provided by the cores of sediment obtained on marine geology operations over the sea ice. Several cores recovered from depths of at least 250 metres below sea level in Peary Channel contain plant fragments and carbonaceous material of terrestrial origin (Horn 1963). One core recovered from 370 metres below sea level in Prince Gustaf Adolf Sea penetrated an ancient soil and stopped in bedrock (personal communication, J. I. Marlowe and G. Vilks, Geological Survey of Canada). The terrace from which this core was obtained extends parallel to Ellef Ringnes Island, and slopes gently seaward, where it is 30 to 50 metres deeper in the vicinity of the Arctic Ocean adjacent to the tip of the drowned headlands.

The over-all evidence supports the hypothesis that at least 400 metres of drowning is present in the offshore areas of the Arctic Islands, particularly over the continental shelf. This amount appears to be progressively less in the inland areas of the channels where ancient, high areas existed. The evidence of deeper soundings in the southeastern parts of the islands, such as 900 metres in eastern Lancaster Sound, indicates that drowning may not have been uniform over the Archipelago. This lack of uniformity suggests differential movement of the earth's crust in different parts of the islands after the close of the Pleistocene epoch.

THE EASTERN CHANNELS

Soundings of the waters of Nares Strait, which lies between the Arctic Ocean and Baffin Bay, and soundings of the waters of Jones and Lancaster sounds revealed a similar development of topography to that of the channels of the western Arctic Islands. In the area underlying Kennedy Channel, Hall Basin, and Robeson Channel (Fig. 6), the submarine topography is somewhat hummocky along the longitudinal profile. However, the regional

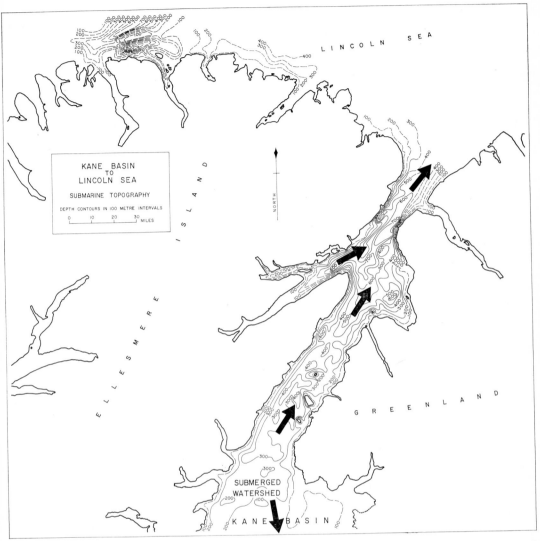

FIGURE 6. Upper Nares Strait. Arrows indicate the direction of flow of valley glaciers from presumed watershed in Kane Basin. Sea floor drops away to north. Hanging tributaries occur about 200–300 metres above main sea floor. Sills are common at mouths of submerged valleys, and a chain of basins presumed to be former paternoster lakes occurs down the length of the channel.

submarine relief drops from a presumed submerged watershed (presently a sill) at a depth of 100 metres in northern Kane Basin to a depth of 400 metres at the entrance to the Lincoln Sea on the Arctic Ocean. Submarine valleys enter from both Greenland and Ellesmere Island, and drop about 200–300 metres as hanging tributaries to the main valley floor, or trunk system, of the northern part of Nares Strait. These features are similar to those in the western Arctic Islands, and suggest a similar origin involving fluvial—glacial erosion and marine submergence. In connection with this physiographic similarity on both sides of the Arctic Islands, a series of basins occurs along the entire length of Robeson Channel. These basins resemble the system of paternoster lakes suggested by Horn for similar features in Peary Channel.

Kane Basin (Fig. 7) is generally shallow in the eastern part, where the depth of water is between 100 and 200 metres. The topography of the bottom is fairly uniform owing to the occurrence of ground moraine 20 to 30 metres thick, according to shallow seismic records. This morainal material was deposited by the receding Humboldt Glacier to the east on the western coast of Greenland. Around the southern perimeter of Kane Basin, a trough is present at depths of 400 metres with smaller troughs leading in to it from the coast of Greenland. This pattern resembling a trunk system also suggests former terrestrial erosion followed by marine submergence. On the western side of Kane Basin the submarine topography is irregular, and the regional slope drops away from the sill in the northern part at depths of 100 to 200 metres, to depths of 500 metres in the southern part adjacent to Smith Sound.

In Smith Sound the regional elevation of the sea floor continues to drop from the Kane Basin sill, and is about 650 metres below sea-level at the northern part of Baffin Bay (Fig. 8). The most striking feature of the topography of Smith Sound is the east-west alignment of topographic features. This is more apparent in the eastern part where headlands and valleys extend from shore, as submarine valleys and ridges, towards the central portion of the sound where depths of 600 metres are recorded. On the eastern side of Smith Sound, a continental shelf does not appear to have developed. Here the submarine topography is a drowned portion of the western coast of Greenland. On the western side of Smith Sound, the topography of the bottom is somewhat more regular but the 600-metre depths occur closer to Ellesmere Island than to Greenland. The submarine contours suggest that a narrow continental shelf does occur off the south-eastern coast of Ellesmere Island. This uniformity of depth may be due to the occurrence of flat-lying, underlying bedrock, or a former erosional surface, and thus represents submergence of an original flat-lying feature. Submergence is suggested here as depths on the east are similar to those on the west, and the topographic features could have developed under the action of subaerial erosion.

In Jones Sound, depths of water have been determined along several longitudinal and transverse lines, but on the whole coverage is inadequate. The soundings indicate that a similar type of submarine topography to that of the northern and western channels is present (Fig. 9). The similarities are as follows: a shallow headward portion, which is located in the western end and appears to be a drowned watershed at depths of 100 metres or less; a long axial trough, which is somewhat hummocky in profile; hanging tributaries occurring at elevations of 300 metres or so above the

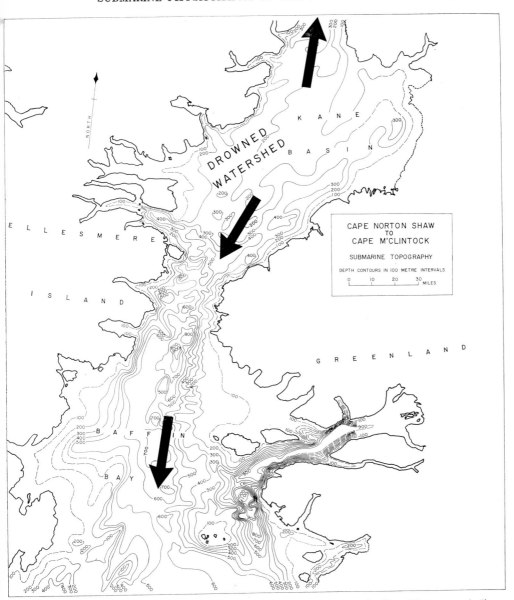

FIGURE 7. Submarine topography of lower Nares Strait and northern Baffin Bay. The arrows indicate the direction of flow of valley glaciers from presumed watershed in Kane Basin. Note increase in depth south of watershed, and the hanging tributaries occurring about 200 metres above the main floor of the straits.

main channel floor; sills at the mouths of the tributaries; glaciers or cirques at the head of some of these tributaries; and a "toeing-up" of the main trough in the area of the continental shelf adjacent to western Baffin Bay. In addition submerged facetted spurs occur between the mouths of tributaries.

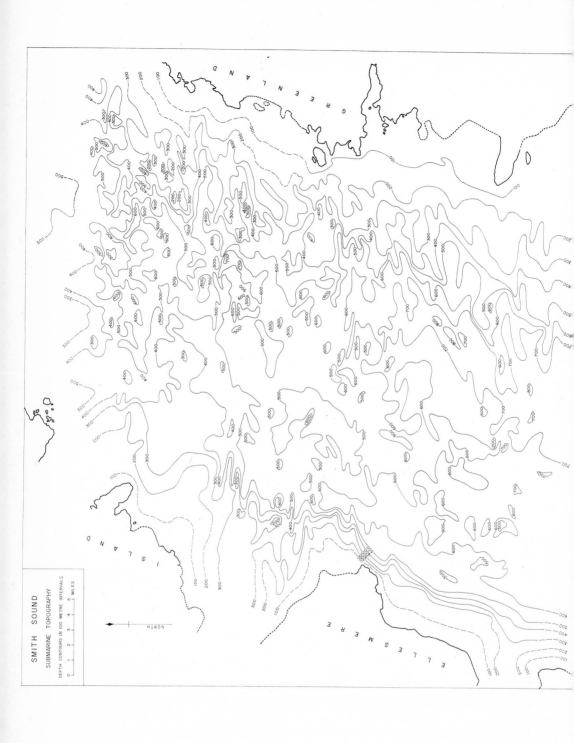

SMITH SOUND

SUBMARINE TOPOGRAPHY

DEPTH CONTOURS IN 100 METRE INTERVALS

0 1 2 3 4 5 MILES

NORTH

Glacier Strait, at the eastern end of Jones Sound between Coburg and Ellesmere islands, is shallow and does not contain a deep axial trough. About 20 to 30 miles farther east, depths greater than 400 metres are present. The configuration of the bathymetric contours, together with the occurrence of this feature in a shallow area adjacent to glacial valleys, suggests that this small basin is a drowned cirque. Presumably a glacier headed in this feature and advanced easterly towards Baffin Bay.

Lady Ann Strait, which lies at the eastern end of Jones Sound between Coburg and Devon islands, is deep close to the shores of both islands, and is the continuation of the axial trough in Jones Sound. The submarine physiography of Jones Sound and adjacent waters appears to have developed according to the following events: fluvial erosion along a pre-Pleistocene drainage system, modification of this drainage system by the action of valley glaciers, and finally submergence. As in other parts of the Arctic Islands, raised marine deposits indicate post-Pleistocene elevation of the land relative to sea level (Craig and Fyles 1960).

In Lancaster Sound (Figs. 10 and 11) the submarine topographic features are similar to those of Jones Sound, except that faulting has occurred along the north side, which adds some complications to the interpretation. However, the hanging U-shaped tributary of Admiralty Inlet, which enters Lancaster Sound on the south side, and the apparent trunk system consisting of the numerous U-shaped hanging tributaries on the north side of Lancaster Sound with cirques at their head and sills at their mouth indicate an origin of fluvial erosion and modification of the topography due to subsequent valley glaciation. This is further substantiated by the fact that Lancaster Sound itself is U-shaped in profile along a transverse section.

NORTHERN AND CENTRAL BAFFIN BAY

In Baffin Bay the bottom slopes from depths of 200 to 400 metres below sea level in the northern part, where the sea floor is continuous with that of Smith Sound, to depths greater than 2300 metres in the central part of the basin (Fig. 7, 12, and 13). In the northern area, which extends south from Greenland, the submarine topography is somewhat hilly and resembles a submerged headland previously exposed to subaerial weathering. This submerged headland drops to a regular sloping surface about 140 miles from shore at depths of 600 metres. Here it merges into a wide terrace, which constitutes an outer continental shelf.

On the eastern side of Baffin Bay (Figs. 12 and 13), the continental shelf is desserted by deep sinuous valleys, which extend from valleys existing

FIGURE 8. Submarine topography of Smith Sound. Note the strong east–west alignment of physiographic features, also the increase in depth of the sea floor from an average of 300–400 metres in the north to 600–700 metres in the south.

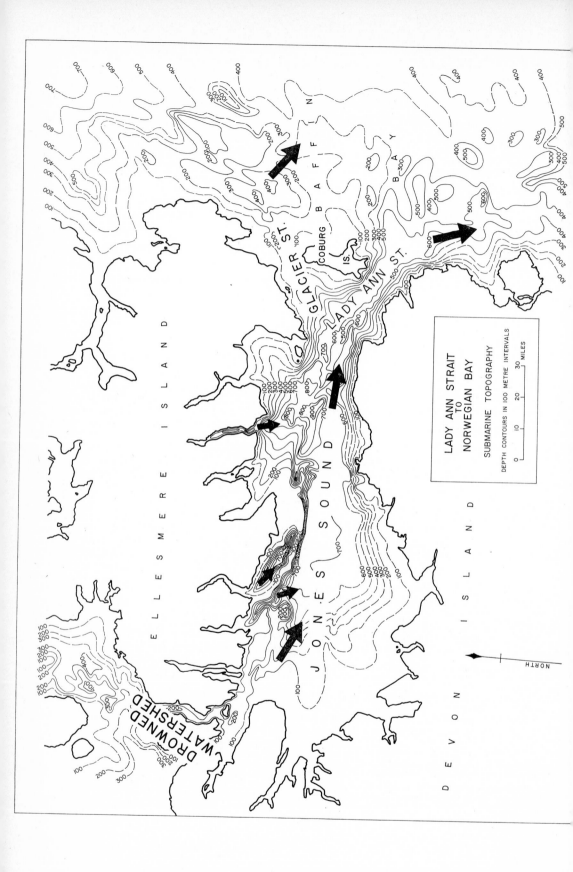

LADY ANN STRAIT
TO
NORWEGIAN BAY

SUBMARINE TOPOGRAPHY

DEPTH CONTOURS IN 100 METRE INTERVALS

0   10   20   30
MILES

BAFFIN

GLACIER ST.

COBURG

IS.

LADY ANN ST.

BAY

ELLESMERE ISLAND

JONES SOUND

DEVON ISLAND

DROWNED WATERSHED

NORTH

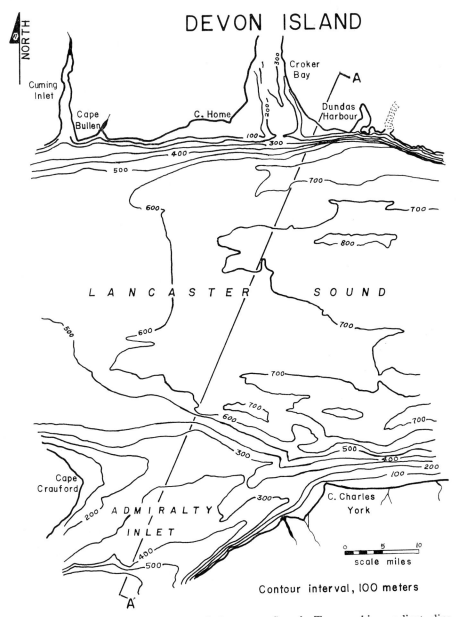

FIGURE 10. Submarine topography of Lancaster Sound. Topographic gradient dips to east. Sill occurs at mouth of Admiralty Inlet, which hangs more than 300 metres above the floor of Lancaster Sound. Croker Bay and Cuming Inlet on the north side of Lancaster Sound show similar features (after Buckley 1963).

FIGURE 9 (*left*). Submarine topography of Jones Sound. Note drowned watershed in western part, U-shaped longitudinal valley in main part, hanging tributaries and associated sills and drowned cirques flanking both sides. Arrows indicate direction of flow of valley glaciers.

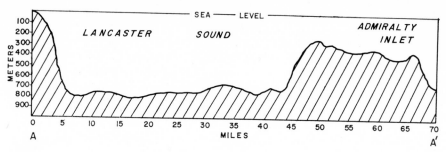

FIGURE 11. Topographic profile of Lancaster Sound. Sides of channels are U-shaped (after Buckley 1963).

along the western coast of Greenland. Similarly, drowned headlands or interfluvial areas occur between these valleys and are contiguous with related features on land. A profile drawn along a headland westerly from Greenland shows a hilly topography extending about 70 miles off shore which resembles a drowned headland at depths of more than 300 metres. From this point seaward the topography drops regularly to 400 and 500 metres at a point 140 miles off shore, and then drops rapidly to 2300 metres in the central part of the basin. In the area between the steep slope and the shore, the sinuous valleys occur at depths of 600 metres. These valleys merge onto the continental shelf in the vicinity of the upper part of the steep, continental slope.

On the west side of Baffin Bay (Fig. 12 and 13), the physical situation is similar except that the continental shelf is narrower and contains more morphologically irregular features. These features can be traced with some difficulty towards headlands and valleys on the adjacent coast. This area of drowned headlands and valleys extends 5 to 70 miles off shore, but is 20 miles in width on the average. As for the east side these submerged features, which extend from headlands and valleys on shore, are truncated at the seaward edge of the shelf by the steep, planar face of the continental slope.

The submarine valleys on both sides of Baffin Bay are U-shaped in profile, have U-shaped hanging tributaries leading into them, and extend into valleys on land occupied by glaciers at the valley head. Thus a development of pre-Pleistocene fluvial erosion was followed by valley glaciation, which subsequently modified the river valleys. Submergence and post-Pleistocene emergence (Fig. 14) appear to have been the final stages in the physiographic history of these shallow-water areas.

The central area, or basin, of Baffin Bay has a depth approximately 5 to 10 times the average depth of all the previously discussed channels of the Arctic. Beneath this central part, the sea floor is featureless and abyssal in aspect, and bears a marked resemblance to a true oceanic basin. This sea floor does not appear to have undergone subaerial erosion. It is bounded on the east and west by steep slopes, which in turn show no evidence of ter-

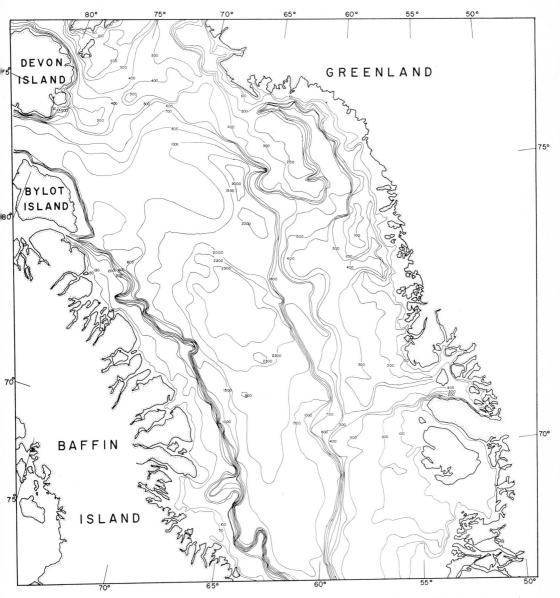

FIGURE 12. Submarine topography of Baffin Bay. The low plain in the central part of the bay is prominent
where it lies between the steep-sided walls forming the continental slope.

restrial erosion or of the physiographic modifications present on the adjacent
continental shelves. These slopes exhibit no evidence of a continuation of
the submerged valleys and ridges that occur on the adjacent shelves.

The origin of the central part of Baffin Bay is unknown. However, on
the basis of a marked contrast in submarine physiography and bathymetry,

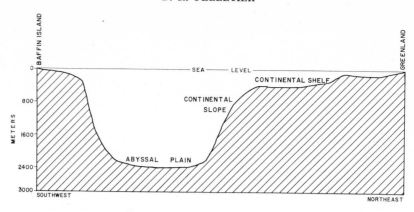

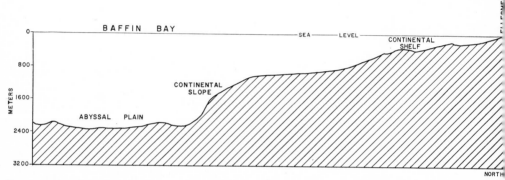

FIGURE 13. Topographic profiles of Baffin Bay. Top figure is a cross-sectional view and lower section is a longitudinal view. The narrow shelf on the west, and the wider shelf on the east side of Baffin Bay are evident in the top figure. Both figures illustrate the steep continental slope.

it is felt that Baffin Bay has a different origin from the island channels. It may have resulted from some form of faulting or down-flexuring of the earth's crust, such tectonic activity perhaps having taken place before the Pleistocene epoch since the basin floor shows no evidence of glacial or fluvial erosion and the continental slope shows no extension of the physiographic lineation occurring on the adjacent continental shelves.

VERTICAL CRUSTAL MOVEMENT

Evidence of vertical crustal movement, exclusive of submergence, which has been discussed previously, is seen in the following: occurrences of raised beaches and marine deposits at various elevations above sea level, a varying faunal suite in different parts of the cores of sediment recovered from the sea floor (personal communication, G. Vilks, Geological Survey of Canada), a change in texture of the sediments in different parts of the core, and the

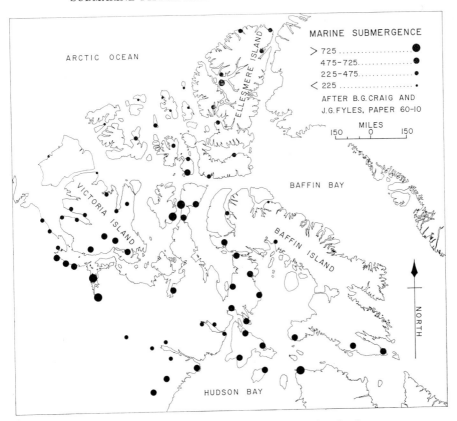

FIGURE 14. Location of raised beaches, Arctic Islands.

occurrence of erratic boulders on the raised beaches. The presence of raised beaches and marine deposits in the central islands (Fig. 14) has been reported by Craig and Fyles (1960). Some of these beaches are dated at 8700 years ± 400 B.P., and occur at elevations up to 800 feet above sea level. These facts, together with the decrease in elevation of younger beaches in a seaward direction, indicate that the Arctic Islands have been rising continually since the close of the Pleistocene. Some of the more seaward beaches are at lower elevations than younger landward beaches, which would indicate differential upwarping.

Other evidence of vertical crustal movement is present in the cores of sediment obtained from marine geological operations over the channel ice (Marlowe and Vilks 1963) in the shallower in-shore areas. These cores show a coarsening in texture of the sediment from the bottom of the core to the top, which indicates the general change from quiescence to a hydrological environment of increasing energy. This change appears to have been induced by crustal uplift, which produced shoaling conditions in the areas that were formerly sites of quieter, deeper-water sedimentation. Increased erosion on land, also an effect of uplift, would contribute coarser material to the depositional site. Therefore it appears that this interplay of physiographic events, the history of sedimentation as shown by the texture of the sediments, and the inferences of a changing hydraulic environment all follow as a consequence chiefly of post-Pleistocene uplift in the Arctic Islands.

Further evidence from the cores, which indicates crustal uplift, is the occurrence of a fairly deep water fauna in the lower part of the core whereas the upper part contains a fauna that exists only in considerably shallower waters. Such faunal sequences generally indicate a decrease in depth of a few hundred metres as suggested by data from F. J. E. Wagner (1962) (see also Pelletier 1963). This zoning suggests that the area from which the cores were taken has risen a distance of 200 to 300 metres (700 to 1000 feet) in the past few thousand years. No accurate dating has been made on this fauna but the estimate is based on a comparison of the layers in the cores with those that have penetrated ancient soil horizons and have thereby presented a datum. This datum has been dissected by valley glaciers that retreated, according to most estimates, about 10,000 years ago. Thus the inference is that the sea bottom together with the adjacent islands has risen several hundred feet in the past few thousand years—certainly since the Pleistocene epoch.

A further line of evidence for a rising land mass in the Arctic is the presence of granite boulders on many of the beaches and low cliffs of sedimentary formations along the arctic coast. These boulders vary up to 3 and 4 feet in diameter, and are somewhat blocky although they may exhibit well-worn edges. As there is no substantial evidence of widespread continental glaciation on the northern islands (the Queen Elizabeth Group in particular) the writer, in collaboration with his colleague A. E. Collin, suggests that these boulders were rafted by means of fragments of an ice-sheet that had broken away from the northern parts of the Archipelago.

Both the writer and Collin have landed on ice that has broken from an ice shelf, and have observed the exceptionally heavy mass of sediments, up to the size of boulders, that is transported by the ice. On one occasion the writer noted a series of boulder ridges on the ice, the ridges increasing in height with distance from the margin of the ice that formerly faced the land. Since each ridge was formed from the run-off of one season, the evidence of several years' accumulation is present on this shelf ice. (The uplift of the older ridges results from ice accumulation under the sheet.)

It is this shelf ice, which breaks away from the coast and drifts with the main arctic circulation, that may eventually pass through to the Atlantic Ocean by means of the inter-island channels. However, along this route it may become grounded and left stranded upon a coastline or island. The writer assumes that such a series of events took place previously when sea level was higher. After melting of the ice, the coarse debris remained on the beach. Since raised beaches extend for a considerable distance towards the centre of the Arctic Archipelago, it is probable that such rafting took place over a wide area of the islands. This would also account for the presence of coarse, unsorted boulders and other sediments lying upon the well-washed highly sorted beach sands and gravels. With the dropping of sea level, sufficient wave energy would be available to remove the finer material but not the coarse, and the latter would remain as a lag deposit.

An independent line of evidence exclusive of sampling and physical observations involves research in the field of geophysics. Gravity measurements by Sobczak *et al.* (1963) over the arctic continental shelf indicate that the area is in isostatic equilibrium, and that no further uplift is expected that would be attributed to ice unloading. This suggests that, although the gravity results are by no means conclusive as yet, the position of the now submerged areas of the continental shelf and adjacent channels is probably not due to ice loading but rather to tectonic activity. If submergence is due to ice loading, then there remains to be explained the existence of the more than 400 metres of water that has been added to the continental shelf since the close of the Pleistocene.

In terms of the raised beaches and the drowned shelf, there may be as much as 600 to 700 metres (or about 2000 feet) of vertical movement that must be considered. Therefore it seems likely that, although some movement is a result of sea-level fluctuations due to loading and melting of ice, most of the vertical movements of the earth's crust must be ascribed to forces that are presumably internal and, perhaps, continental in magnitude.

Summary and Conclusions

In summary there appears to be ample evidence that a Tertiary drainage system existed as suggested by Fortier and Morley, and that the present inter-island channels are the result of submergence of this ancient drainage system. The inference that topographic modifications of this drainage system are due chiefly to the action of valley glaciers appears to be substantiated, although the action of thin sheets of ice upon the interfluvial areas has not been overlooked. Submergence is established on the basis of physiography for all parts of the coastal submarine areas. Equally strong is the evidence for emergence, which is seen in raised beaches, the sedimentary texture and varying fauna of the bottom cores, and stranded ice-rafted boulders.

The theory of simple ice loading and release of stress after ice melting does not appear sufficient to explain the over-all vertical movement of 2000 feet, especially in the narrow span of time allotted for such movement. Therefore, exclusive of the presumed tectonism associated with the origin of Baffin Bay, it appears that a general tectonic force acted over the entire Archipelago, and may be in operation at present.

From a physiographic and tectonic point of view both northern Greenland and the Arctic Islands have identical histories. Nares Strait appears to be part of a former river system complete with watersheds and tributaries, and it is likely that geological structure controlled the original drainage system. It does appear that, since the close of the Pleistocene epoch, the crustal movement of the arctic islands was vertical and not horizontal. This vertical movement initiated more rapid and coarser sedimentation and brought about shoaling conditions in near-shore waters. It caused a relative lowering of sea level and brought the sea floor and its associated older sediments and a deeper water fossil fauna to shallower depths. Finally it triggered a sequence of physiographic processes that resulted in the formation of raised beaches all over the islands. Therefore, by assessing the interplay of tectonic, physiographic, and hydrological forces and some of the ecological conditions, it has been possible to relate the development of submarine physiography to crustal movements.

REFERENCES

BUCKLEY, D. E. (1963). Bottom Sediments of Lancaster Sound, District of Franklin. M.Sc. Thesis, University of Western Ontario, London, Ontario.

COLLIN, A. E. (1961). Oceanographic activities of the Polar Continental Shelf Project. J. Fish. Res. Bd. Can., *18*: 243–258.

COLLIN, A. E. and DUNBAR, M. J. (1964). Physical oceanography in Arctic Canada. Oceanogr. Mar. Biol. Ann. Rev., 2: 45–75.

CRAIG, B. G. and FYLES, J. G. (1960). Pleistocene geology of Arctic Canada. Geol. Surv., Can., Paper 60–10.

EATON, R. M. (1961). Borden Island to Meighen Island (Hydrographic chart based on soundings by Polar Continental Shelf Project, with accompanying report). Can. Hydrographic Serv., File F.S. 3072 S.C.

FORTIER, Y. O. and MORLEY, L. W. (1956). Geological unity of the Arctic Islands. Trans. Roy. Soc. Can., Ser. 3, Can. Comm. on Oceanog., *50*: 3–12.

HORN, D. R. (1963). Marine geology, Peary Channel, District of Franklin, Polar Continental Shelf Project. Geol. Surv. Can., Paper 63–11.

HUNKINS, K. L., EWING, M., HEEZEN, B. C., and MENZIES, R. J. (1960). Biological and geological observations on the first photographs of the Arctic Ocean deep-sea floor. Limnol. and Oceanogr., 5 (No. 2): 154–161.

MANCHESTER, K. S. (1964). Geophysical Investigations between Canada and Greenland. Unpublished M.Sc. Thesis, Dalhousie Inst. Oceanogr., Halifax, N.S.

MARLOWE, J. I. (1964). Marine geology, western part of Prince Gustaf Adolf Sea, District of Franklin (Polar Continental Shelf Project). Bedford Inst. Oceanogr., Dartmouth, N.S., Rept. B.I.O. 64–9.

MARLOWE, J. I. and VILKS, G. (1963). Marine geology, eastern part of Prince Gustaf Adolf Sea, District of Franklin (Polar Continental Shelf Project). Geol. Surv. Can., Paper 62–22.

OSTENSO, N. A. (1962). Geophysical investigations of the Arctic Ocean Basin. Univ. Wisconsin Geophys. and Polar Res. Center, Res. Rept. Ser. no. 62–4.

PELLETIER, B. R. (1961). Progress report of the Submarine Geology Group, Polar Continental Shelf Project. Geol. Surv. Can., Topical Rept. No. 47.

——— (1962). Submarine geology program, Polar Continental Shelf Project, Isachsen, District of Franklin. Geol. Surv. Can., Paper 61–21.

——— (1963). Contributions of the Marine Geology Unit of the Geological Survey of Canada to the Polar Continental Shelf Project, District of Franklin, 1962. Geol. Surv. Can., Topical Rept. No. 69.

PERRY, R. B. (1961). A study of the marine sediments of the Canadian Eastern Arctic Archipelago. Fish. Res. Bd. Can., MS Rept. no. 89.

ST. ONGE, D. (1964). Geomorphology of Ellef Ringnes Island, Northwest Territories. Geograph. Branch Can. Mem. 11.

SHEPARD, F. P. (1963). Submarine Geology. Harper's Geoscience Series; New York, Evanston, and London: Harper and Row Publisher.

SOBCZAK, L. W. (1963). Regional gravity survey of the Sverdrup Islands and vicinity with map. Dominion Observatories Gravity Map Ser. no. 11—Sverdrup Islands.

SOBCZAK, L. W., WEBER, J. R., GOODACRE, A. K., and BISSOM, J. L. (1963). Preliminary results of gravity surveys in the Queen Elizabeth Islands with maps. Dominion Observatories Gravity Map Ser. no. 12—Sverdrup Islands; no. 13—Prince Patrick Island; no. 14—Melville Island; no. 15—Devon Island.

VILKS, G. (1964). Foraminiferal study of East Bay, MacKenzie King Island, District of Franklin (Polar Continental Shelf Project). Bedford Inst. Oceanogr., Dartmouth, N.S., Rept. B.I.O. 64-4.

WAGNER, F. J. E. (1962). Faunal report, Submarine Geology Program, Polar Continental Shelf Project, Isachsen, District of Franklin. Geol. Surv. Can., Paper 61–27.

———— (1964). Faunal report–II, Marine Geology Program, Polar Continental Shelf Project, Isachsen, District of Franklin. Bedford Inst. Oceanogr., Dartmouth, N.S., Rept. B.I.O. 64–1.

MORPHOLOGICAL AND GEOPHYSICAL STUDIES ON THE EASTERN SEABOARD OF CANADA: THE NOVA SCOTIAN SHELF

Jon Berger, A. E. Cok, J. E. Blanchard, and M. J. Keen

THE NOVA SCOTIAN SHELF is considered a northern extension of the submerged Atlantic Coastal Plain (Murray 1961), with its topographical and sedimentological characteristics similar to those of the continental shelf off the eastern United States, except for minor features resulting from Pleistocene glaciation. Investigations of the shelf were conducted by the Dalhousie Institute of Oceanography to establish its general character and to outline areas for future detailed studies.

The Institute, in co-operation with the Departments of Geology and Physics at Dalhousie University, also conducted a series of seismic crustal studies over the Nova Scotian Shelf, as part of Canada's contribution to the Upper Mantle Project.

During 1960 and 1961 the Canadian Hydrographic Service made a survey of various areas of the Nova Scotian Shelf, taking bottom samples and increasing the density of depth soundings over those done previously. Traverses followed a series of parallel paths running approximately north-south at intervals ranging from 1 to 2 km. The density of the traverse lines was increased threefold in some areas. Information collected from this survey provided data on the morphology of the Nova Scotian Shelf (see Fig 1).

In 1962 three seismic recording stations were established on the Nova Scotia mainland and two profiles were shot; one (shot line A in Fig. 2) some 300 km in length off shore and parallel to the coast, and the other (shot line B) perpendicular to the coast from Halifax to the edge of the shelf. In 1963 recording equipment was located on Sable Island, which lies at the edge of the shelf. Five long-range profiles (C_1–C_5) were obtained as well as a partially reversed profile on the island itself, which was used to determine its sedimentary structure. The seismic investigations provided the information required for the crustal studies.

In addition to the work described in this paper, a qualitative analysis of sediment types on the Nova Scotian Shelf area to the south of Halifax, and a quantitative analysis of sediments and morphology of the Laurentian Channel, have been completed by the Dalhousie Institute of Oceanography.

The Institute will soon make available the results of a study of the general geology of the Nova Scotian Shelf, including a detailed sedimentological analysis of bottom samples.

The Nova Scotian Shelf (Fig. 1) covers approximately 120,000 km². It is bounded on the northwest by the mainland of Nova Scotia and the island of Cape Breton. Toward the northeast it ends abruptly at the Laurentian Trough, which separates it from the Grand Banks of Newfoundland. The southeastern extremity is 230 km from the Nova Scotian coast. The shelf narrows to 100 km to the southwest and is separated from Georges Bank by another channel, normal to the coast, known as the Northeast Trough.

Morphology of the Nova Scotian Shelf

The general pattern of the shelf is one of pronounced relief. The morphology is usually complicated.

The most northerly portion of the shelf, and morphologically one of the least complex, is the narrow tongue found between the Laurentian Trough and Cape Breton Island north of Scatari Island. Contours are widely spaced, indicating a gently undulating surface, and the margin of the shelf is very linear, as in other cases where it abuts on the Laurentian Channel.

South of Cape Breton Island and to the east of 61° 00′ W the most intensively "dissected" portions of the shelf occur. At approximately 45° 30′ N near the edge of the shelf a series of elongate and deep channels about 2 km in width and as deep as 380 metres run normal to the Laurentian Trough, but are separated from it by a levee-like ridge lying at an average depth of 130 metres. These small channels trend, discontinuously, west to Chedabucto Bay.

An extremely irregular but shallow zone averaging 90 metres in depth occupies an area 25 km in width slightly north of 45° N. Nautical charts show a portion of the area as Misaine Bank. The morphology is sufficiently irregular to cast doubts on the validity of considering this a banks area.

Directly south of the Misaine Bank area another highly "dissected" zone is marked by depths in excess of 350 metres, separating numerous extremely flat-topped highs at an almost uniform repth of 85 metres. The seaward terminus of this zone becomes pinched out near the Laurentian Trough.

Continuing south, the remainder of the shelf between 57° 15′ W and 59° 00′ W is occupied mostly by Banquereau Bank, which lies at an average depth of 62 metres except for the east side, which shoals to a depth of 28 metres. A tongue-like westerly extension of Banquereau Bank is separated from Middle Bank by a depression 18 km in width. This depression has a minimum depth of 130 metres and is connected with another elongate area north of the Sable Island Bank. It terminates at the shelf margin at "The Gully," a deep canyon cutting into the shelf between Sable Island Bank and Banquereau Bank.

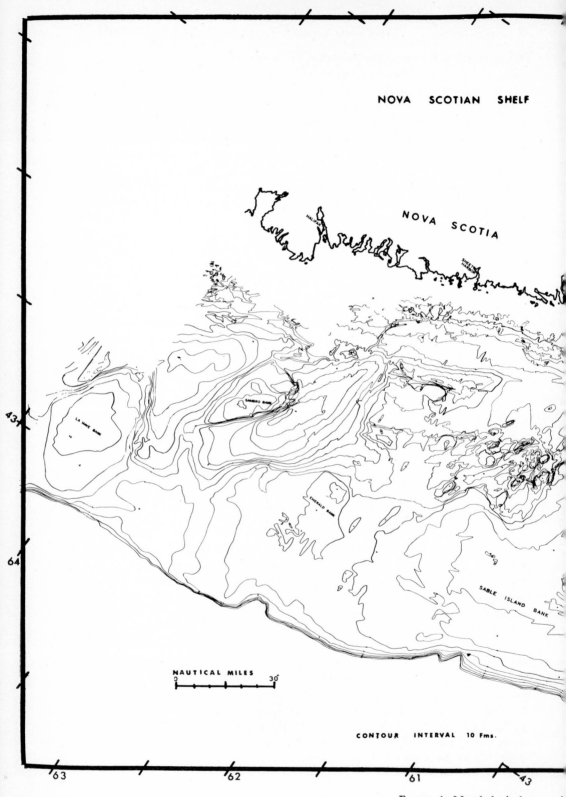

NOVA SCOTIAN SHELF

NOVA SCOTIA

HALIFAX

SHEET HARB.

LA HAVE BANK

SAMBRO BANK

EMERALD BANK

SABLE ISLAND BANK

NAUTICAL MILES

0   30'

CONTOUR INTERVAL 10 Fms.

43°

43°

63°   62°   61°   43°

FIGURE 1. Morphological map of

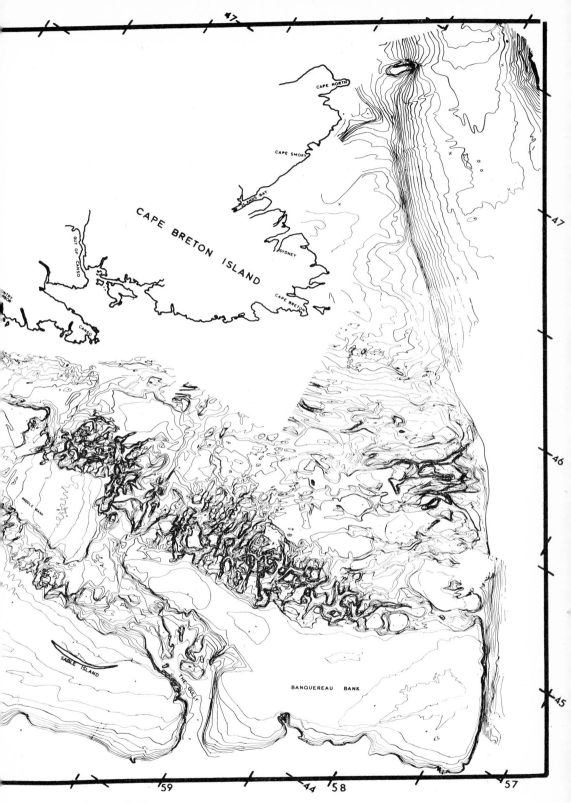

ova Scotian Continental Shelf.

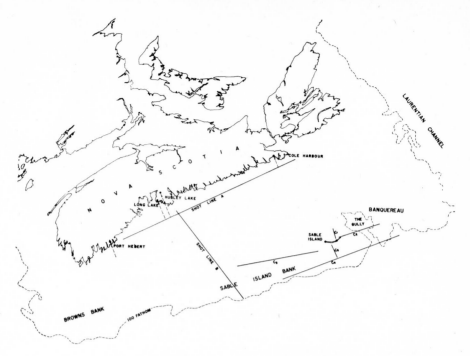

FIGURE 2. Refraction profiles and station locations.

From Cape Canso south along the northeastern shore of Nova Scotia a narrow band approximately 20 km in width out to a depth of 186 metres reflects the embayed nature of the mainland. The "Ria"-like structures gradually disappear, and a more regular topography appears, which characterizes the middle and outer shelf as far south as the Northeast Trough.

Two large, smooth basins separated by Sambro Bank lie to the south of Halifax. They are approximately 140 km long and 40 km in width with the long axis of each basin trending to the northeast.

The remainder of the central and outer portions of the shelf to the south has a very smooth surface marked by several small regular banks such as Emerald, LaHave, and Browns banks, separated from one another by gentle depressions.

Figures 3 A–E illustrate the changing appearance of the shelf exposed if sea level is reduced in stages by 274 metres (i.e. 150 fathoms). Most of the shelf east of Cape Breton Island, Sable Island Bank, and the tops of the flat-topped highs north of Banquereau Bank would emerge at 90 metres. Additional lowering for another 90 metres would not change the general appearance of the shelf but would show basinal areas within the margin of the shelf isolated from the sea. With a drop in sea level to the maximum of 273 metres (Fig. 3E) three isolated submerged areas would still exist within the shelf.

FIGURE 3A. Emergent portions of the Nova Scotian Shelf if present-day sea level is
reduced to 55 metres. Areas deeper than this are shaded black.

FIGURE 3B. Emergent portions of the Nova Scotian Shelf if present-day sea level is
reduced to 92 metres. Areas deeper than this are shaded black.

FIGURE 3C. Emergent portions of the Nova Scotian Shelf if present-day sea level is reduced to 128 metres. Areas deeper than this are shaded black.

FIGURE 3D. Emergent portions of the Nova Scotian Shelf if present-day sea level is reduced to 183 metres. Areas deeper than this are shaded black.

FIGURE 3E. Emergent portions of the Nova Scotian Shelf if present-day sea level is reduced to 274 metres. Areas deeper than this are shaded black.

The portion of the shelf east of Cape Breton Island is readily related to continental features. Emergence or submergence of the shelf here would not alter the general shape of this area. The moderate relief is a continuation of that seen on land where the Carboniferous strata have been eroded to a relatively smooth lowland. Carboniferous rocks are found well below tide level, and coal seams that extend for thousands of metres beyond the shore are being mined. Recent work at Dalhousie University indicates that Carboniferous strata may well outcrop on the edge of the Laurentian Channel. One might consider this section a drowned Carboniferous headland rather than a true shelf.

Another portion of the shelf that seems to be closely related to shore areas is that part adjacent to the southeastern coast of Nova Scotia between Cape Canso and St. Margaret's Bay, which is underlain by folded and faulted Precambrian Meguma slates and quartzites. The "Ria" structure of the shore line continues below sea level to depths of 186 metres and for a distance of 20 km from shore. The irregular topography probably continues well beyond 20 km but is covered by younger, relatively flat-lying sediments. Consequently a submerged fall line is inferred at the margin of this portion of the shelf even though it is imperfectly formed.

The seismic investigations suggest that the remainder of the shelf, namely the central and outer shelf, is probably underlain by sediments similar in age to those found off the eastern coast of the United States, which are mainly post-Jurassic and Tertiary in age.

The parallel and elongate nature of the surface structures at the north-eastern end of the Nova Scotian Shelf, together with the presence of zones of alternating depth (varying between 90 and 380 metres), points to bed-rock control. For this reason it is impossible to relate the morphological character of the shelf exclusively to a glacial origin. It is probable, however, that the deposition of sediment by ice, either as moraine material or as a result of extensive ice rafting, blocked outlets to the open ocean from basinal areas well within the margin of the shelf. Thus, the random positions of the flat-topped highs within the complex elongate zone directly north of Banquereau Bank are best explained by deposition of glacial sediments.

It seems likely that the line of marginal banks from the Grand Banks of Newfoundland to Georges Bank is a depositional feature, related to pre-Pleistocene sedimentation rather than to a series of morainic deposits as has been postulated (Johnson 1925). It is difficult to envisage such uniformity for ice depositional forms.

The presence of depths to 380 metres and of many filled basins, indicated by flattening and abrupt reduction in slope at depths as great as 350 metres, leads one to the inference that structures seen on the shelf were formed when the shelf was more than 350 metres above sea level. It is difficult to attempt to date such an emergence; however, it is presumed to have occur-red sometime after the Cretaceous.

SEISMIC CRUSTAL STUDIES OF THE NOVA SCOTIAN SHELF

Willmore and Tolmie (1956) have published the results of short-range seismic refraction profiles on Sable Island. Extensive investigations con-ducted in an area to the southwest of Sable Island and off the eastern coast of the United States by the Lamont Geological Observatory have been described by Officer and Ewing (1954). Part of the Dalhousie programme has been reported by Barrett et al. (1964).

The seismic equipment used at Dalhousie consisted of two sets of very-low-frequency refraction amplifiers, each equipped with recording oscillo-graphs. The geophones were the moving-coil type with resonant frequencies of 2 cps.

At each recording station a spread of five or six geophones was arranged in line with the proposed direction of the profile, with a distance of 350 to 500 metres between them, so that the arrivals of energy could be recorded over a total length of up to 2.5 km. Energy sources were supplied by the electrical detonation of R.C.N. 300-lb. and 50-lb. depth charges from the C.N.A.V. "Sackville." Information regarding apparent and true velocities as well as dip was obtained.

Figure 4 shows the section inferred by Barrett et al. (1964) from the 1962 profile. The seismic stations were situated on outcrops of the Meguma Series, which consists of conformable quartzites and slates. Travel time plots from local shooting established compressional wave velocities in this

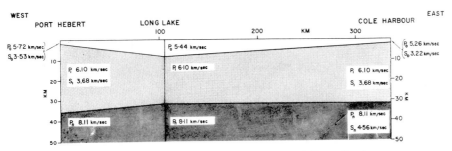

FIGURE 4. Crustal section, Atlantic Coast of Nova Scotia.

material varying from 5.26 to 5.72 km/sec, and shear wave velocities between 3.22 and 3.53 km/sec. These rocks on the mainland of Nova Scotia extend to a depth of 2.1 km under Cole Harbour and 2.8 km under Port Hebert. Under the Meguma there was evidence of a single layer characterized by a compressional velocity of 6.10 km/sec and shear velocity of 3.68 km/sec extending down to a mantle with compressional velocity of 8.11 km/sec and shear velocity of 4.56 km/sec. The thickness of the crust at Cole Harbour was 32.6 km, and at Port Hebert 36.3 km. (The assumptions made in the analysis of refraction experiments by elementary methods should be kept in mind; see Barrett *et al.* (1964).)

Having established with a reversed profile the true velocities of the crustal and upper mantle material, a second profile was obtained perpendicular to the coast extending from Long Lake near Halifax, seaward to the edge of the continental shelf, some 150 km to the southeast. Here, the travel time plot revealed 8.3 km of Meguma rocks with a compressional velocity of 5.44 km/sec. Although no sedimentary velocities were indicated by the travel time plots, it is known that accumulations of sediment exist under the off-coast shot points. Estimates as to the thicknesses and velocities of these sediments were obtained from the profiles compiled by Officer and Ewing (1964), and corrections were applied to the travel times. The resulting compressional velocity was 6.10 km/sec in the continental crustal layer, and 8.11 km/sec for the mantle. The total crustal thickness under Long Lake is 32.8 km.

A partially reversed local profile some 20 km in length on Sable Island revealed three sedimentary layers with a total thickness of 4.6 km, these layers overlying a basement material with a compressional velocity of 5.86 km/sec. However, on the long-range profile C_5 (see Figs. 2 and 5), which extended out from the west end of the island and which was essentially a continuation of the local profile, the basement velocity appeared as 5.40 km/sec. This layer extended some 9.2 km down to a depth of 13.8 km, where a layer of compressional velocity 6.25 km/sec was encountered. The compressional velocity in the mantle was 8.0 km/sec, and assuming that these velocities are the true velocities, a total crustal thickness of 35.0 km is indicated.

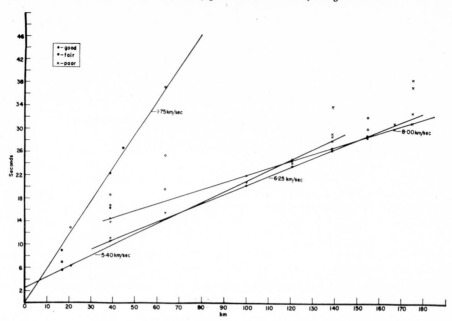

FIGURE 5. Profile C$_5$ travel time plot.

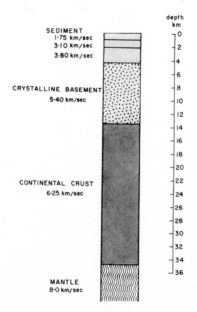

FIGURE 6. Crustal section, Sable Island.

ACKNOWLEDGMENTS

We thank the following organizations for their help and co-operation: the Department of Mines and Technical Surveys (and especially the Canadian Hydrographic Service), the Fisheries Research Board, the Nova Scotia Research Foundation, and the Royal Canadian Navy. The work is supported by the National Research Council and the Defence Research Board.

REFERENCES

BARRETT, D. L., BERRY, M., BLANCHARD, J. E., KEEN, M. J., and McALLISTER, R. E. (1964). Seismic studies on the Eastern Seaboard of Canada: The Atlantic Coast of Nova Scotia. Can. J. Earth Sci., *1*: 10–22.

JOHNSON, D. W. (1925). New England-Acadian Shoreline. New York: John Wiley & Sons.

MURRAY, G. E. (1961). Geology of the Atlantic and Gulf Coastal Province of North America. New York: Harper.

OFFICER, C. B. and EWING, M. (1954). Geophysical investigations in the emerged and submerged Atlantic Coastal Plain. Bull. Geol. Soc. Amer., *65*: 653–670.

WILLMORE, P. L. and TOLMIE, R. (1956). Geophysical observations on the history and structure of Sable Island. Trans. Roy. Soc. Can., Ser. 3, Can. Comm. on Oceanogr., *50*: 13–20.

UNDERWATER GRAVITY MEASUREMENTS IN THE GULF OF ST. LAWRENCE

A. K. Goodacre and E. Nyland

DURING 1962 and 1963 the Dominion Observatory carried out a regional underwater gravity survey in the Gulf of St. Lawrence. The purpose of the survey was to extend the regional gravity coverage of Canada for geodetic and crustal studies. The area surveyed lies entirely within the Appalachian geological province, and it was expected that gravity data would provide important information regarding the continuity of geological structures across the Gulf between the mainland and Newfoundland.

Because this was the first major underwater gravimeter work undertaken by the Observatory, particular attention was paid to the development of sound survey procedures. Approximately 450 stations were established at 13-km intervals over a major portion of the Gulf southwest of a line joining the Gaspé Peninsula and Cape Breton Island (Fig. 1).

This paper presents the results of this survey in the form of a Bouguer anomaly map and a structural interpretation of the major gravitational features. A preliminary interpretation and accompanying Bouguer anomaly map of scale 1 : 760,320 have been presented elsewhere (Goodacre 1964). Principal facts for the gravity stations may be obtained on request from the Dominion Observatory.

THE SURVEY EQUIPMENT AND OPERATION

The gravity measurements were carried out in successive years aboard the ships M.V. "North Star VI" and M.V. "Theta," which were chartered by the Department of Mines and Technical Surveys. Each ship was about 50 metres long and equipped with an echo sounder, radar, and Decca navigation receiver. The underwater gravimeter employed was manufactured by LaCoste and Romberg of Austin, Texas, and was essentially a land gravimeter unit mounted in gimbal rings in a water-tight case (Fig. 2). The gravimeter was a remotely controlled instrument with various indications, including level and instrument setting, being displayed on a control panel operated on the ship's deck. The instrument, which has a low drift rate and good repeatability characteristics, gave gravity values accurate to about two or three tenths of a milligal, with reference to a land base station.

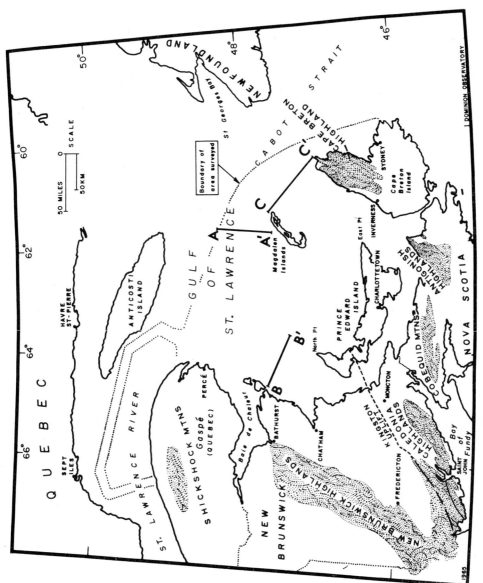

FIGURE 1. Map showing the area surveyed and location of sections A–A', B–B', and C–C' discussed in the text.

FIGURE 2. Photograph of underwater gravimeter being lowered overboard.

A neoprene-covered 48-conductor cable, 3.7 cm in diameter and 365 metres long, provided the electrical connection between the gravimeter and the control unit and was used also for lowering and raising the instrument to and from the ocean floor. An especially constructed winch with two drums mounted on a single shaft was necessary to maintain a continuous connection between the gravimeter and control box. A large drum contained the main hoisting cable, while a smaller drum contained a connecting cable that went to the control unit. These two cables were connected at the winch and the smaller cable unwound onto the deck while the gravimeter and main cable were lowered in the water. The hydraulic winch had smooth, positive control both in the forward and reverse directions, allowing the gravimeter to be handled safely under practically all conditions.

The winch and its diesel-powered pumping unit comprised a self-contained system, which was easy to remove from one ship and install on another. In each case they were installed on the foredeck in view of the bridge to assist the officers in keeping the ship on station. About ten minutes were needed to position the ship and lower and raise the instrument, while four or five minutes were needed to read the gravimeter. At no time was it necessary to anchor the ship while taking a gravity reading.

A Decca electronic navigation system, which provides excellent coverage of the Gulf of St. Lawrence area, was used to position the underwater gravity measurements. Although constant errors in absolute position of up to 500 metres may be present in this system for some parts of the Gulf, experience indicated the gravity stations could be positioned to within 100 metres on repeated visits. Depth measurements, used to correct observed gravity readings to sea level, were taken with a Kelvin Hughes echo sounder and are estimated to have an accuracy of about two per cent.

Stations were placed in a grid pattern and in addition two traverses were made across anomalous features. The gravimeter was read at the beginning and end of each cruise at a land gravity station in order to place the measurements on an absolute basis and to determine a drift rate. During the course of the survey readings at several stations at sea were taken on repeated visits in order to obtain an estimate of the accuracy of the work. Two days were lost owing to rough weather but, on the average, readings at 15 stations were done each day.

REDUCTION OF THE MEASUREMENTS

In order to reduce the gravity observations to a common elevation datum the observed gravity readings were first extrapolated to the surface of the sea taking into account the normal free air vertical gradient of gravity and the attraction of the layer of water above the instrument:

$$(1) \qquad g_s = g_{obs}(1 - 2d/R) + 4\pi\gamma\phi d$$
$$= (g_{obs} - 0.223d) \text{ mgal,}$$

where g_s is the gravity at the surface, g_{obs} is the gravity observed, R is the radius of the earth, γ is the gravitational constant, ϕ is the density of sea water (1.03 g/cc), and d is the observed depth in metres. A correction for marine tide (Bott 1961) was not applied; the maximum error in neglecting this correction is of the order of one tenth of a milligal.

In this paper, only Bouguer anomalies are considered. These were calculated in the usual way by adding to the surface gravity value a correction of $+0.069d$ mgal for the mass deficiency of water with respect to rock of standard density 2.67 g/cc and subtracting a theoretical gravity value at the station computed from the international gravity formula:

$$\Delta g \text{ (Bouguer)} = (g_{obs} - 0.154d) \text{ milligals.}$$

The error in the Bouguer anomaly at an underwater station due to errors in observed gravity, observed depth, navigation, adopted vertical gradient, and the error in neglecting marine tide correction was estimated to be of the order of a milligal.

Description and Significance of the Bouguer Anomalies

The Bouguer anomaly values in the map area (Fig. 3) have a range of over 100 mgal varying from less than −70 mgal to more than +30 mgal. The regional value of the anomalies is −20 to −30 mgal over the highland areas of western New Brunswick and −50 to −60 mgal over the highland areas of Quebec, north of the St. Lawrence River. Over the St. Lawrence River the regional value is −30 to −40 mgal, while over the southern Gulf and the lowland areas of New Brunswick and Nova Scotia it is between 0 and −10 mgal. Negative anomalies of −10 to −15 mgal are also observed adjacent to the highland areas of New Brunswick and Nova Scotia.

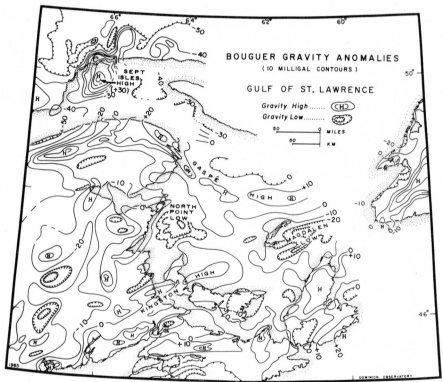

Figure 3. Bouguer anomaly map: Gulf of St. Lawrence.

Three areas of negative anomaly occur in the Gulf. An approximately circular negative anomaly of −30 mgal which is observed 100 km east of Bathurst and 50 km north of North Point, Prince Edward Island, will be termed the North Point low. A highly irregular negative anomaly varying from −35 to −5 mgal occurs between the Magdalen Islands and Cape Breton Island and will be called the Magdalen low. Other negative anomalies reaching minimum values of about −15 mgal are found over eastern Prince Edward Island and off the west coast of Cape Breton Island.

Several positive anomaly belts occur on land. In southeast New Brunswick near the Bay of Fundy, a positive anomaly belt of +20 to +30 mgal is observed over the Caledonian Highland, while similar belts are found over the Cobequid, Antigonish, and Cape Breton Highland areas of Nova Scotia. Two other positive anomaly belts can be traced into the Gulf. One occurs over the Shickshock Mountains of the Gaspé Peninsula and has been traced south and east to the limit of the survey some 50 km north of the Magdalen Islands. This will be referred to as the Gaspé high. The other positive anomaly belt, which is associated on land with the Kingston uplift and will be called the Kingston high, extends northeast from New Brunswick through Prince Edward Island and terminates about 65 km from the Magdalen Islands. Although not completely defined, what appears to be a circular positive anomaly with a¹ peak value of +30 mgal is located in the St. Lawrence River south of Sept.-Iles. This will be called the Sept-Iles high.

Two conclusions may be obtained directly from the gravity information: (1) The general inverse correlation between the Bouguer anomalies and station elevations and the near zero mean value of the anomalies in lowland areas indicate that the crust in the area, as a whole, is nearly in isostatic equilibrium. Local exceptions apparently occur however, in the St. Lawrence River, in Gaspé, and in the uplifted highland areas of southeastern New Brunswick and of Nova Scotia. (2) The underwater measurements also show that the crust under the Gulf is continental in character, as several gravitational features observed on land can be traced considerable distances off shore.

INTERPRETATION OF THE BOUGUER ANOMALIES

(a) General Relationships to Geological Structure

The geology of the Canadian Appalachian Region has been described by Lang (1961) as follows:

Most of the region is underlain by folded and faulted Palaeozoic sedimentary and volcanic strata and Palaeozoic intrusions; the latter include both granitic and ultrabasic types. The northwestern boundary of the region is a long, arcuate fault or zone of faults extending from Lake Champlain at least as far as the Gulf of St. Lawrence. East and south of this line the strata have been folded and faulted by successive periods of orogeny, along axes that strike north-easterly. Thus strata of different kinds and ages, and belts of intrusive rocks, form northeasterly trending bands or lineaments. Three principal periods of orogeny—called the Taconic, the Acadian, and the Appalachian—have been recognized. The Taconic occurred at the close of the Ordovician, the Acadian during the Devonian, and the Appalachian at the close of the Palaeozoic. The Taconic disturbances were fairly widespread; the Acadian were more so, affecting areas that were previously affected by the Taconic and some that were not; but the Appalachian orogeny, which was a major feature in parts of the United States, was of minor and local importance in the Canadian part of the region.

An overlay of gravity contours on a tectonic map of the area prepared from the work of Neale, Beland, Potter, and Poole (1961) (Fig. 4) shows that large-scale gravity trends on land correlate with certain structural units. Positive anomalies in Gaspé correlate with a narrow zone of rocks folded during the Taconic orogeny in Ordovician time, which is characterized by a belt of basic and ultrabasic intrusions. Negative anomalies in the highland areas of New Brunswick appear to overlay Devonian granite bodies as suggested by Garland (1953). Positive anomalies in New Brunswick and Nova Scotia correlate with Precambrian blocks uplifted in late Palaeozoic time while adjacent negative anomalies are associated with deep sedimentary basins.

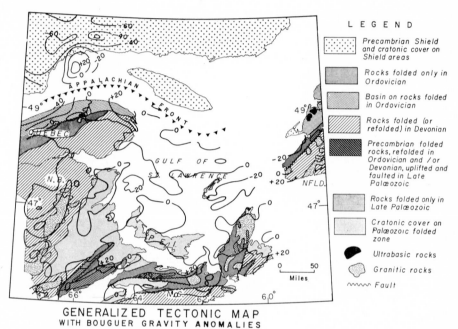

GENERALIZED TECTONIC MAP
WITH BOUGUER GRAVITY ANOMALIES

FIGURE 4. Combined tectonic and gravity map: Gulf of St. Lawrence.

The gravity anomalies over the Gulf have patterns similar to those observed on land and therefore are likely to derive from similar sources. For example, negative anomalies are probably caused by either low-density Devonian granite masses or low-density sedimentary strata. Positive anomaly belts extending into the Gulf appear to be caused either by lithological changes within the basement or by uplift of the basement rocks (Garland 1953; Tanner and Uffen 1960).

A major problem in the interpretation of the gravity field over the Gulf is the determination of the graviational effects of the sedimentary strata. Published values of seismic depths to crystalline basement (McConnell and McTaggart-Cowan 1963; Willmore and Scheidegger 1956), which have been plotted in Figure 5, show little correlation with the gravity anomalies generally (Fig. 3). This lack of correlation may be due to inadequate seismic

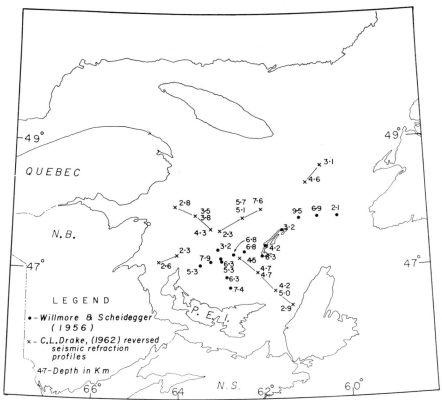

GULF OF ST LAWRENCE
SEISMIC OBSERVATIONS OF SEDIMENTARY THICKNESS

FIGURE 5. Seismic depths to basement: Gulf of St. Lawrence.

data, but more likely it indicates that the variations in the gravity anomalies are not produced entirely by variations in the thickness of the sedimentary rocks. According to the seismic data the sedimentary strata vary from 2.3 to 7.9 km within the surveyed area. Drake's seismic velocities (McConnell and McTaggart-Cowen 1963) combined with Nafe and Drake's (1957) seismic velocity–density relationship indicate that the average density contrast between the sedimentary strata and crystalline basement is about +0.2 g/cc. If these values are correct, the mass deficiency of the sedimentary rocks would depress the gravity field from 20 to 70 mgal; from this we must conclude that a mass excess exists at depth, which could be the expression of high-density basement rocks underlying the Gulf, or due to crustal thinning, or due to both of these.

On the other hand the regional gravity value of −30 to −40 mgal over the St. Lawrence River north of Gaspé and near Anticosti Island indicate a considerable mass deficiency, which may not be due entirely to a thick prism of sedimentary rock. Geological evidence (Howie and Cumming

1962) and diamond drilling by the oil industry show that the stratum underlying Anticosti Island does not exceed 2 km; such a thickness would account for less than one half the total gravity anomaly. This suggests that a major part of the anomaly originates from sources deeper within the crust and may be due to thickening towards the north of the granitic layer as suggested by Tanner and Uffen (1960).

(b) Discussion of Individual Anomalies

No further explanation of the regional gravity field is offered here, and in the interpretations that follow a regional value of about −5 mgal will be assumed for all of the Lower Gulf.

The Gaspé high, which is about 40 km wide and at least 250 km long, is the most prominent anomaly mapped during the underwater gravity survey. This positive anomaly appears to outline an arcuate extension of the Taconic folded zone of Gaspé (Fig. 4) and its presence in the Gulf tends to confirm the suggestion of King (1951) that the rocks of northwestern Newfoundland correlate with those of the Gaspé Peninsula rather than those of Cape Breton Island.

In the Gaspé Peninsula the positive anomaly over the Shickshock Mountains trends east and is interpreted by Tanner and Uffen (1960) as being produced by high-density basic rocks of the Shickshock Series. Near the eastern end of the peninsula the gravity contours change direction and trend southeast. Here the nature of the variations of gravity across the strike of the anomaly, including the maximum observed horizontal gradient and maximum change in gravity, indicates that the structure producing the anomaly cannot be more than 2 km deep and must have a density contrast with respect to surrounding rock of at least +0.2 g/cc. Its actual density is at least 2.8 g/cc since the mean density of the area is 2.63 g/cc (Tanner and Uffen 1960). Therefore, although there is no surface expression of basic rocks in the area where the gravity anomalies reach maximum values, it is safe to conclude that the Gaspé high is produced by a belt of basic rocks consisting of upthrust blocks or dyke-like bodies rather than an uplift of the normal crystalline basement. The nature of the gravity field north of the Magdalen Islands producing this positive anomaly belt indicates that the postulated structure of basic rocks could be as deep as 6 or 8 km. This value agrees well with the seismic depth to basement of 7.5 km obtained by Drake (see McConnell and McTaggart-Cowen 1963). It is shown in section A–A[1] (Fig. 6) that in this area the observed gravity field is similar to that produced by an infinitely long rectangular prism 3 km thick and 40 km wide with its upper surface at a depth of 6.5 km. A density contrast of +0.3 g/cc has been used since this value was obtained by Tanner and Uffen (1960) by direct density measurements of basic volcanic and surrounding sedimentary rocks from the Gaspé area.

The Kingston high (Fig. 3) is a linear positive anomaly that trends northeast from the vicinity of Moncton across New Brunswick and Prince Edward

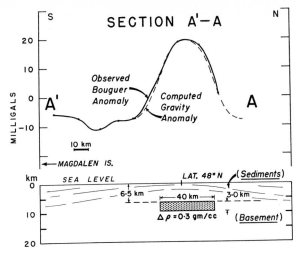

FIGURE 6. Bouguer anomaly profile A–A', north of Magdalen Islands.

Island into the Gulf. It is about 50 km wide and 200 km long and similar in dimensions to other linear positive anomalies observed over the highland areas in New Brunswick and Nova Scotia. Howie and Cumming (1962) have noted that the basement blocks forming the Caledonia Highlands, the Cobequid Mountains, and Cape Breton Highlands have similar lengths. These similarities suggest the Kingston high is the gravitational expression of such a basement block extending into the Gulf.

Since the Kingston high lies along the Kingston uplift (Howie and Cumming 1962), the gravity anomaly is produced at least partly by an uplifted pre-Carboniferous basement; some of the contribution may be due to density variations within the basement itself as has been suggested by Garland (1953) for the portion of the gravity high that is observed on land. This interpretation is confirmed in New Brunswick from drilling results (Howie and Cumming 1962), which indicate sedimentary thicknesses of the order of 1 km with a minimum depth to basement of about 0.3 km. If we assume a density contrast of +0.2 g/cc between the structure producing the anomaly and the overlying sediments, an uplift of 1 km would account for one half the observed anomaly, suggesting that a significant portion is due to density variations within the basement. Gravity and seismic evidence indicates that the structure producing the Kingston high may be at a greater depth under the Gulf than on land. The underwater gravity measurements show that the top of the structure could be as deep as 6 km, a depth consistent with seismic data for the area, which indicate the presence of 5 to 7 km of sediments. A few drilling results in Prince Edward Island, which suggest that both the magnitude of the Kingston uplift and the thickness of the sedimentary cover increase to the northeast, are consistent with these geophysical data.

The Sept-Iles high, although not clearly defined, appears to be circular in shape, to have a diameter of approximately 50 km, and to exhibit an over-all variation in gravity of 70 mgal. The magnitude and extent of this anomaly indicate that its source has a considerable mass excess with respect to surrounding crustal rocks. For example, if the source is assumed to approximate a vertical cylinder of radius 25 km and density contrast $+0.3$ g/cc, the length of the cylinder would be 8 km or more, depending upon the depth of burial of the cylinder. Gabbro and anorthosite observed at Sept-Iles near the edge of the anomaly (Faessler 1942) may reflect the composition of the source of the Sept-Iles high. The problem of how much the anorthosite contributes to this positive anomaly will need investigation as other anorthosites are known to produce negative gravity anomalies (Thompson and Garland 1957).

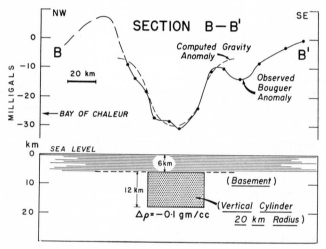

FIGURE 7. Bouguer anomaly profile B–B', east of Bathurst.

The North Point low is similar in appearance to three other negative anomalies in New Brunswick which have been associated with Devonian granite formations (Garland 1953). Seismic depths to basement (Fig. 4) indicate the anomaly is due to a source other than thick sediments and therefore may indicate an extension under the Gulf of the Devonian granite belt of New Brunswick. The residual anomaly of -25 mgal in section B–B' can be accounted for on the assumption that the granite mass approximates a vertical cylinder of radius 20 km, length 12 km, with upper surface at a depth of 6 km, and density contrast of -0.1 g/cc with respect to surrounding basement (Fig. 7).

The Magdalen low, which is about 40 km wide and at least 70 km long, trends towards St. Georges Bay, Newfoundland. This anomaly is characterized by steep gradients, which show that the top of the structure is no deeper than 4 km. In fact, the structure may be shallower, as the general character of the gravity field suggests the actual gradients are higher than the present station spacing can measure.

Geological and seismic evidence (Fig. 5) indicates the possibility that there is a considerable thickness of Palaeozoic sediments between the Magdalen Islands and Cape Breton Island. In particular, stratigraphic information indicates that about 7 km of sediments are present in the St. Georges Bay area of Newfoundland (Baird and Cote 1964), and drill hole information indicates that there is at least 4 km of sediments under the eastern end of Prince Edward Island (Howie and Cumming 1962). It seems most likely that the variations in the gravity field are produced by density variations within the sedimentary column. These density variations may be related to any or all of the unconformities found between the sedimentary sequences in the Appalachian region. For example, on the Magdalen Islands, folded, eroded Mississippian sediments and volcanics are overlain by relatively flat Pennsylvanian strata while unconformities within Mississippian strata and between Carboniferous sediments and earlier folded, metamorphosed rocks are observed elsewhere in the Maritimes (Eardley 1962).

A possible structure, shown in section C–C' (Fig. 8), with a density contrast of −0.2 g/cc and a trapezoidal section about 40 km wide and 3

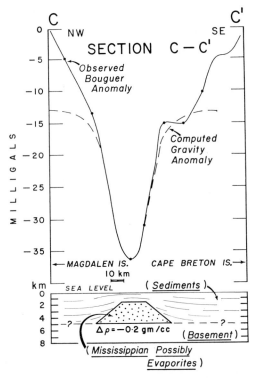

Figure 8. Bouguer anomaly profile C–C', east of Magdalen Islands.

km thick with its top at a depth of 2 km could produce an anomaly similar
to that observed. Alternatively, a combination of Devonian granite, characteristic of the widespread Acadian orogeny, and basic volcanic rocks intrud-
ing sediments may produce the anomaly. However, this is speculative, and
further information, including accurate seismic data, is needed to determine
the nature of the source of the Magdalen low.

Variations in thickness and composition of late-Palaeozoic rocks (Fig. 4)
may also be responsible for the gravity anomalies between the eastern end
of Prince Edward Island and Cape Breton Island (Fig. 9) (Garland 1953;
Howie and Cumming 1962). For example, the circular negative gravity

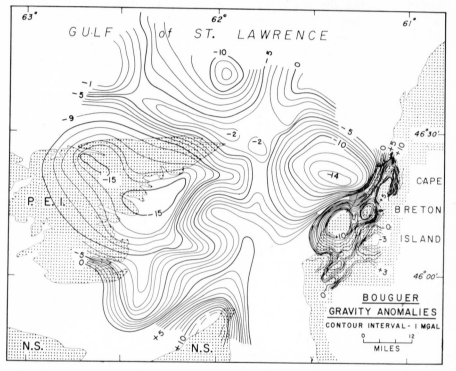

FIGURE 9. Bouguer anomaly map: Prince Edward Island–Cape Breton Island area.

anomaly of −14 mgal west of Inverness, Cape Breton Island, could be
produced by a layer of evaporites 2 km thick, 40 km across, and 2 km
deep with a density contrast of −0.2 g/cc. A band of less-negative anomalies
with a peak value of −2 mgal lying just north of Prince Edward Island
may represent an area of uplift in the pre-Carboniferous basement. A
ridge 2 km high and 14 km wide with its upper surface at a depth of 4 km,
and having a density of 0.2 g/cc greater than surrounding sediments, would
produce a similar anomaly. This gravity anomaly shows some correlation
with a strong widespread positive magnetic anomaly between Prince Edward
Island and Cape Breton Island (Fig. 10). However, the magnetic anomaly
is wider and its axis lies somewhat to the south of the gravity anomaly.

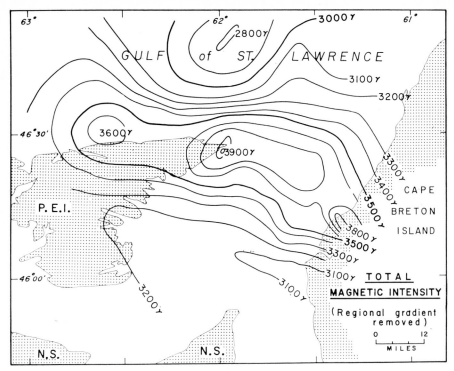

FIGURE 10. Residual total magnetic intensity map: Prince Edward Island–Cape Breton Island area.

It is interesting to note that the value of 3900 γ is one of the highest anomalies occurring within the lower Gulf of St. Lawrence and the value of 2800 γ, 35 km to the north, is the lowest. The relationship between the gravity and magnetic anomalies is not clear and further investigation appears necessary.

CONCLUSION

The initial aims to develop underwater gravity survey techniques and extend land gravity coverage were realized. The gravity measurements show that the crust under the Gulf is continental in character, is nearly in isostatic equilibrium, and undergoes a change in the vicinity of the Gaspé Peninsula. Several positive and negative anomalies have been outlined. The Gaspé high, the North Point low, and the Kingston high indicate extensions of early or middle Palaeozoic basement features under the Gulf while the Magdalen low and anomalies between Prince Edward Island and Cape Breton Island appear to be produced by variations within the late-Palaeozoic sedimentary column. In particular, the Gaspé high outlines a continuation of a major structure from the Gaspé Peninsula towards Newfoundland and tends to resolve the problem of apparent structural discontinuities between Newfoundland and the mainland.

Further seismic information for the Gulf is needed to provide better control for the gravity interpretation and, of course, further regional gravity coverage to the northeast and more detailed investigations over anomalous areas are desirable.

ACKNOWLEDGMENTS

The authors gratefully acknowledge the encouragement and advice of Dr. M. J. S. Innes during both the field programme and preparation of this paper as well as the contribution of Dr. J. E. Blanchard, who supplied unpublished material on rock densities and gravity computations from the files of the Geophysics Division of the Nova Scotia Research Foundation.

Mr. D. Barrett prepared the residual total magnetic intensity map while studying at the Dalhousie Institute of Oceanography under Dr. M. J. Keen. Dr. Keen's comments and discussions are much appreciated, as are those of Mr. J. G. Tanner of the Dominion Observatory.

REFERENCES

BAIRD, D. M. and COTE, P. R. (1964). Lower Carboniferous sedimentary rocks of southwestern Newfoundland and their relation to similar strata in western Cape Breton Island. Can. Mining Met. Bull., 509–520.

BOTT, M. H. P. (1961). A gravity survey off the cost of north-east England. Proc. Yorkshire Geol. Soc., 33, pt. I, no. 1.

DRAKE, C. L. (1962). Unpublished seismic profiles.

EARDLEY, A. J. (1962). Structural Geology of North America, 2nd ed. New York: Harper and Row.

FAESSLER, C. (1942). Sept-Iles Area, north shore of St. Lawrence, Saguenay County. Geol. Rept. II, Dept. Mines, Prov. of Quebec.

GARLAND, G. D. (1953). Gravity measurements in the Maritime Provinces. Pub. Dom. Obs., 16, no. 7.

GOODACRE, A. K. (1964). Preliminary results of underwater gravity surveys in the Gulf of St. Lawrence, with map. Gravity Map Ser. no. 46, Dominion Observatory.

HOWIE, R. D. and CUMMING, L. M. (1962). Basement features of the Canadian Appalachians. Geol. Surv. Can., Bull. 89.

KING, P. B. (1951). The Tectonics of Middle North America. Princeton, N.J.: Princeton Univ. Press.

LANG, A. H. (1961). A preliminary study of Canadian Metallogenic Provinces. Geol. Surv. Can., Paper 60–33.

McCONNELL, JR., R. K. and McTAGGART-COWAN, G. H. (1963). Crustal seismic refraction profiles. A compilation. Inst. of Earth Sciences, Univ. of Toronto, Sci. Rep. no. 8, Contract AF 19(628)–22, pp. 39–40.

NAFE, J. E. and DRAKE, C. L. (1957). Variation with depth in shallow and deep water marine sediments of porosity, density and the velocities of compressional and shear waves. Geophysics, 22 (no. 3): 523–552.

NEALE, R. W., BELAND, J., POTTER, R. R., and POOLE, W. H. (1961). A preliminary tectonic map of the Canadian Appalachian region based on age of folding. Can. Mining Met. Bull., 54 (no. 593): 687–694.

TANNER, J. G. and UFFEN, R. J. (1960). Gravity anomalies in the Gaspé Peninsula, Quebec. Pub. Dom. Obs., 21, no. 5.

THOMPSON, L. D. G. and GARLAND, G. D. (1957). Gravity measurements in Quebec, south of latitude 52° N. Pub. Dom. Obs., 19, no. 4.

WILLMORE, P. L. and SCHEIDEGGER, A. E. (1956). Seismic observations in the Gulf of St. Lawrence. Trans. Roy Soc. Can., Ser. 3, Can. Comm. on Oceanogr., 50: 21–38.

THE CABOT FAULT ZONE*

H. L. Cameron

THE OCCURRENCE of large faults of possible transcurrent type in the Maritime Provinces has been known for a long time (Fletcher 1883; Goldthwait 1924), and a generalized map (Fig. 1†) showing the then known ones was published in 1956 (Cameron 1956). It remained for J. T. Wilson to compare the main linear feature, which he has named the Cabot fault, to the Great Glen fault of Scotland. He further suggested that if continental drift is a valid concept, the Cabot fault may be an extension of the Great Glen fault and therefore a fundamental earth fracture of great importance (Wilson 1962). The purpose of the present paper is to describe the various segments of the Cabot fault zone with their related faults and fold structures and to evaluate the data in the light of the Wilson hypothesis.

From the assembled data it is concluded that no continuous throughgoing surface fracture exists from New foundland to Boston. It is found that in the Precambrian basement or adjacent to it, there are large continuous faults which resemble the Great Glen fault, but even here they appear to exist in parallel pairs. In the overlying Palaeozoic and Mesozoic sediments and volcanics the fractures appear to form zones that are made up of a mosaic of fault blocks. Local evidence for movement is valid only in the Precambrian and pre-Carboniferous, and then only indirectly, as will be illustrated on the Coolavee-Aspy fault of Cape Breton Island. Here local grabens on the south of the fault suggest a pre-Mississippian right-hand movement. The movements on the various fault segments cutting the Palaeozoic and Mesozoic rocks are directly related to adjustments of the fault block mosaic. As such they do not necessarily indicate the movement or movements on the basement fracture. It seems probable that a number of movements have taken place along the basement fracture, both right- and left-hand movements of relatively small size.

The essential parallelism between the main segments of the zone and the Appalachian trends is noted. This, combined with the wedge and ramp nature of the fault slices, suggests that the main segments are essentially strike thrusts caused by compression of the geosyncline. The branch fractures, particularly the east–west zone through central Nova Scotia and the newly

---

*Published with the permission of the Nova Scotia Research Foundation and the Royal Air Force.
†For Figure 1, see envelope at the back of the book.

postulated one just south of New York (Drake and Woodward 1963), appear to be transcurrent to the main geosynclinal fold trends.

CABOT FAULT (NEWFOUNDLAND)

This segment of the fault zone has been mapped by Baird (1959), Betz (1943), and others. A fault defining the Codroy River Valley was known to exist, and it was extended tentatively to the Deer Lake Valley, where it would connect with the White Bay fault. Field mapping and topography indicated the presence of a parallel fault, which defines the linear coastline of the northwest section of Newfoundland. Until very recently statements about the relationship between topography and faulting had to be taken as the conclusions of the writer. Today radar offers a new look at topography and, hence, indirectly, at the geology. In Figure 2, a radar photograph

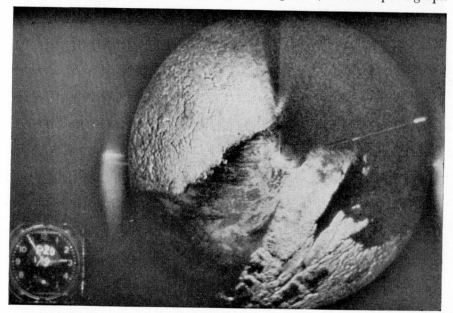

FIGURE 2. Radar photo of Newfoundland showing Codroy–White Bay faults.

taken by the Royal Air Force, the linear valleys show clearly and offer convincing evidence for their fault origin. Figure 3 shows the northwest coast; its linear aspect has been interpreted as due to faulting.

COOLAVEE-ASPY FAULT (CAPE BRETON ISLAND)

In 1883 Hugh Fletcher of the Geological Survey of Canada noted the long, straight scarp extending from Money Point to the Aspy River, and suggested that it was a fault trace. In discussing the physiography of Nova Scotia Goldthwait (1924) not only called the scarp a fault, but also specu-

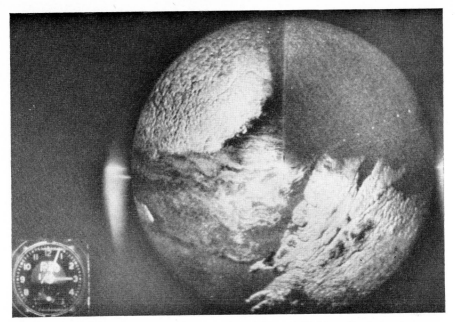

FIGURE 3. Radar photo, northwest lobe of Newfoundland.

lated on other linear features, including the west coast, saying that all belonged to one great system. With the advent of air photographs the fault nature of the scarp and river valley became obvious, the actual fracture being visible at the head of the Aspy Valley (Figs. 4 to 7). The south segment of the fault was mapped in the Margaree area in 1947 (Cameron 1948). Again a long, straight scarp is present extending from Margaree Forks to the Big Interval. The Northeast Margaree River follows it for part of the way but diverges so often that it is not surprising that the fault was unrecognized until air photographs gave a continuous view of the scarp (Fig. 8). This central section is of importance in any attempted determination of fault movement.

FAULT MOVEMENT

In the Aspy River valley southeast of the fault there exists a wedge of Mississippian strata down-faulted on the northwest side adjacent to the fault. The southeast contact appears to be a normal overlap on the Precambrian basement complex. A similar situation exists in the Margaree area, where Mississippian strata are in contact with the Precambrian at Coolavee (Fig. 9, Tectonic Map of Nova Scotia*). These two areas are interpreted as grabens formed in pre-Mississippian times by a right-hand movement on the Coolavee-Aspy fault, which has a slight zig-zag form. A dextral movement would

*For Figures 9, 10, and 11, see envelope at the back of the book.

FIGURE 4. Aspy fault, northeast coast.

have resulted in tension at the two ends, with resultant grabens. These were filled in the Mississippian, and later small movements on the fault brought about the present conditions.

PARALLEL FAULTS

The existence of faults parallel to the Aspy was suspected by Goldthwait, and confirmed by Neale (1955). The existence of a parallel off-shore fault is strongly suggested by the submarine topography and by the aeromagnetic surveys of the Geological Survey of Canada (Figs. 10 and 11). It has been tentatively mapped as an extension of the Hollow fault of Cape George, and, if valid, gives a continuous line of fracture from mainland Nova Scotia to the north end of Newfoundland. The southwest extension of the Coolavee-

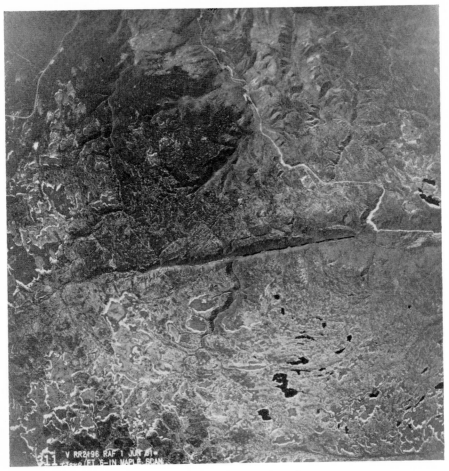

FIGURE 5. Aspy fault, central section.

Aspy fault is not well defined and it may not be continuous. The obvious possible extensions swing south, and near the Strait of Canso form a family of faults curving to meet the east-west double fracture system of the Chedabucto Bay–Guysborough River (see Fig. 1).

HOLLOW FAULT–PICTOU GAP ZONE

The Hollow fault is a clearly defined fracture, which comes ashore at Malignant Cove and extends, with minor interruptions, to the vicinity of French River (Figs. 12, 13, 14). From this point west to the Cobequid fault there is a fracture zone defining the south margin of the Pictou (or Stellarton) Coal Field. This field is a lens-shaped block, with the north margin defined by two or more single faults. It is believed that this block

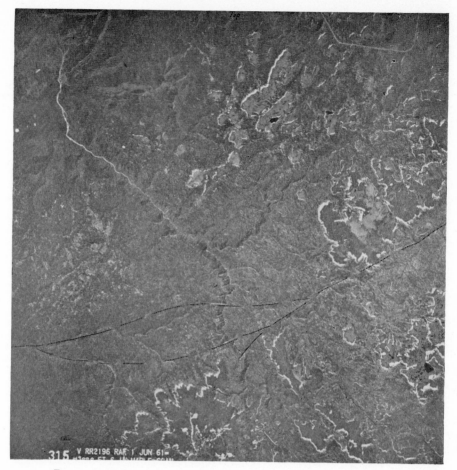

FIGURE 6. Coolavee fault (northeast Margaree–Cheticamp River area).

was formed by movements on pre-Carboniferous faults. A right-hand movement of the blocks on the Hollow fault would create tension in the zone
where this fracture changed strike (Fig. 1) to produce a local basin. The
coal seams of Stellarton show every evidence of local deposition and accumulation in such a local basin.

Stratigraphic relationships on the Hollow fault and the East River–St.
Mary's fault suggest that they are high-angle thrusts. This would make
the Pictou-Antigonish Highland a wedge block upraised by compressional
forces. Similar conditions are found in the Cobequid Hills and the northwest
segment of Newfoundland. The block to the south of the Pictou-Antigonish
Highland and the Meguma massif is a "ramp" block, with outward-dipping
thrusts on both sides. The White Bay block of Newfoundland is a similar
ramp block.

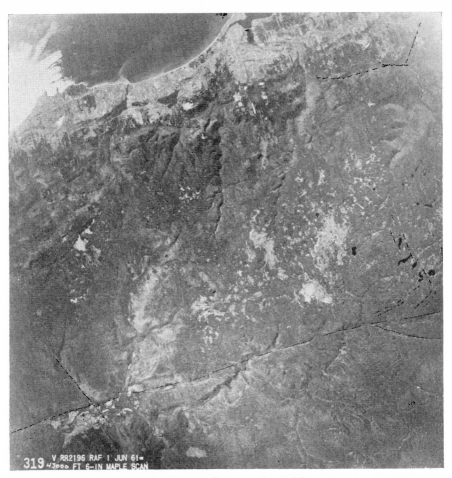

FIGURE 7. Coolavee fault, northeast Margaree.

COBEQUID FAULT

The south side of the Cobequid Hills is a fault scarp remarkable for its straightness. It extends in an almost perfectly straight line from near Truro to Cape Chignecto, a distance of 70 miles. A parallel fault on the north side extends about 35 miles from Earltown to River Philip, where the scarp becomes subdued and Pennsylvanian strata overlap on the Cobequid complex. The pre-Carboniferous fault continues west, as shown on Figure 1, and can be traced readily on the aeromagnetic map (Fig. 15*). The Cobequid block is believed to be a wedge block bounded by inward-dipping thrusts. It is postulated to have been uplifted periodically during the Palaeozoic beginning in the Devonian, and at least three times during the Carboniferous. The wedge hypothesis would explain such repeated uplift. However,

*For Figure 15, see envelope at the back of the book.

FIGURE 8. Coolavee fault (Margaree Forks–Big Intervale section).

the presence of a narrow graben just south of the hills has often been cited as evidence against the Cobequid fault being a thrust. This graben can be explained by a right-hand movement of the Cobequid block along the Hollow fault, which has already been postulated to explain the formation of the Pictou Coal Field basin.

BAY OF FUNDY–GULF OF MAINE–MASSACHUSETTS

The existence of a large fault or faults in this area was first suspected by Johnson (1935). On the basis of profiles, both ordinary and projected, he mapped a fault extending from near Cape Chignecto to southwest of Grand Manan Island, which he named the Fundy fault. Recent work, both seismic and aeromagnetic, tends to confirm Johnson's hypothesis. The faults shown

FIGURE 12. Hollow fault, Araisag area.

on Figure 1 are based mainly on seismic work by Ewing, Worzel, and others (see Drake, Worzel, and Beckman 1954). It is interesting that workers at Woods Hole have recently decided that the north side of Georges Bank is probably a fault. Its strike is parallel to the transcurrent Kelvin fault recently mapped by C. L. Drake and H. P. Woodward (1963).

OTHER MAJOR FAULTS

The Chedabucto Bay–Guysborough double fault system is the most important next to the Cabot zone. The Chedabucto fault extends east to the St. Lawrence Canyon, and west to near Truro. It resembles the Kelvin transcurrent fault, which also occurs as a major flex in the regional trend of the Appalachian folding.

FIGURE 13. Hollow fault, Merigomish area.

The Meguma faults are a system of transverse faults of post-Devonian pre-Carboniferous age. Some are as long as the mapped segments of the Cabot zone and have measurable horizontal displacements of 2 miles. Those east of Halifax are all left-handed, while those west of Halifax are right-handed. Vertical movements on these faults appear to be minor, though in one case the removal of a syncline on the upthrown block indicates a displacement of at least 2000 feet.

SUMMARY AND CONCLUSIONS

The various segments of the Cabot fault zone have been described briefly beginning at the northeast. These appear to form a zone of parallel faults, which are alternately wedge-shaped upward and downward to form wedge

FIGURE 14. Hollow fault, west of the Pictou Coalfield.

and ramp blocks. The majority appear to be high-angle thrusts and their horizontal movements have been small. The age of the original fracture system is tentatively Devonian, but may be older. It is probably related to and controlled by the trends of the Appalachian geosyncline. Movements on the original fault zone and between the fault blocks resulted in a basin and range topography and local basins that largely controlled the Mississippian and Pennsylvanian deposition.

The trend of the main fault zone is parallel, or sub-parallel, to the regional trends and does not have the cross-cutting relationship of a transcurrent fault. Only the Chedabucto offset resembles a transcurrent fault, or swing plus offset, similar to the newly postulated Kelvin fault.

Indirect evidence at Coolavee, Aspy, and south of the Cobequids suggests a relatively small right-hand movement of less than 2 miles. Direct evidence suggests that the main movements have been high-angle thrusts caused by compression, which is believed to have been part of the Appalachian geosynclinal collapse. In the light of the numerous parallel faults and the Minch fault (Dearnley 1962) it is suggested that the Great Glen and its adjacent faults be re-examined for high-angle thrust relationships. The present evidence indicates that the resemblance between the Great Glen fault and the Cabot fault is not very striking.

References

BAIRD, D. (1959). Geol. Surv. Can., Map 47–1959.

BETZ, FREDERICK (1943). Late Paleozoic faulting in western Newfoundland. Bull. Geol. Soc. Amer., *54*: 687–706.

CAMERON, H. L. (1948). The Margaree and Cheticamp Map-areas. Geol. Surv. Can., Paper 48–11.

———— (1956). Tectonics of the Maritimes. Trans. Roy. Soc. Can., Ser. 3, Sec. IV, *50*: 45–52.

DEARNLEY, R. (1962). An outline of the Lewisian complex of the Outer Hebrides in relation to that of the Scottish mainland. Quart. J. Geol. Soc. London, *118*: 143–176.

DRAKE, C. L. and WOODWARD, H. P. (1963).—Appalachian curvature, wrench faulting and offshore structures. Trans. N.Y. Acad. Sci., Ser. 2, *26*: 48–63.

DRAKE, C. L., WORZEL, J., and BECKMANN, W. (1954). Investigations of the emerged and submerged Atlantic Plain, Part IX. Bull. Geol. Soc. Amer., *65*: 957–970.

FLETCHER, H. (1883). Geology of Northern Cape Breton. Ann. Rept. Geol. Surv. Can.

GOLDTHWAIT, J. W. (1924).—Physiography of Nova Scotia. Geol. Surv. Can., Mem. 140.

JOHNSON, D. (1935).—New England–Acadian Shoreline. New York: McGraw-Hill Book Co., Inc.

NEALE, R. W. (1955). Geol. Surv. Can., Papers, 55–13, 55–23, 55–24.

WILSON, J. T. (1962). The Cabot fault. Nature, *195*: 135–138.